NAVIGATIONS2COLLEGE 2022-23

Pacific Northwest Colleges *and* Universities

including

The Cascadian Bioregion

Alaska, British Columbia, Washington, Oregon, Idaho, Montana, N. California

Equitable and Inclusive Access to Higher Education and Training is a Matter of Social and Economic Justice

Cover Photograph by Richard Krieger
https://www.gaiafineartphotography.com/

Colleges and Universities of the Pacific Northwest

Editor: Sarah D. Silver, sarah@navigations2college.org
Book designer: Chris Molé, booksavvystudio.com
Cover photograph: Richard Krieger www.gaiafineartphotography.com

A Publication of:
N2C
Navigations2College
Ashland, Oregon USA 97520-3436

First Edition August 2022

Library of Congress Control Number: 2022908889
ISBN: 9780578266190.

Printed in the United States of America

This book is dedicated to

Jennifer Marsden

College and Career Coordinator at Ashland High School, Oregon
for her deep commitment to and passionate support of her students' aspirations

and to the

Volunteer Mentors, College and Career Coordinators, and Counselors
who work with the State of Oregon's ASPIRE Mentorship Program
and to all others who aspire to inspire our youth to be adventurous explorers
of pathways to post-secondary training and education that can lead them to
self-sufficient and self-fulfilled futures.

Paradise Trail, Mt Rainier, Oregon

Contents

Beach near Bandon, Oregon

The Cascadian Bioregion

The colleges and universities profiled in this guided exploration of Pacific Northwest Colleges and Universities are located within or adjacent to the **Cascadia Bioregion,** a region defined by the great waterways that sustain it.

Our PNW higher education institutions take full advantage of their distinct locations by designing innovative programs of study and unique opportunities for experiential learning and hands-on research on the natural environments, socio-economics, and rich cultural heritages of this beautiful and varied bioregion.

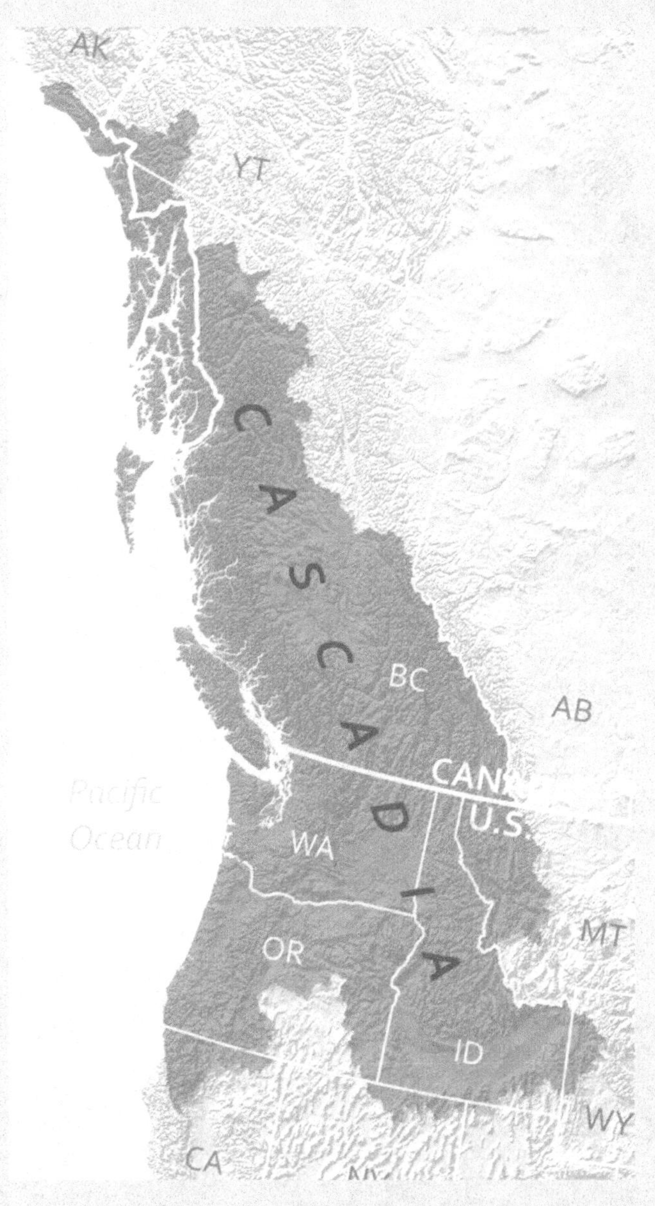

Environmental stewardship and resource sustainability are the primary reasons for defining a bioregion. As you read the Location descriptions in each of the College Profiles, you will discover the many different environments within the bioregion, from the Arctic

waters to the Northern California coast and the farmlands of the Palouse and Willamette Valleys to the highest mountain ranges.

We include a sample of British Columbia colleges and universities because of B.C.'s Cascadian geography and because these institutions welcome U.S. students, have many unique programs, and can be financially competitive for some families. U.S. federal student loans can be used for Canadian higher education costs.

The majority of the states in this PNW regional guidebook share a border with Canada. The area from Vancouver, B.C., through Seattle, Washington, and down to Portland, Oregon, is recognized as a megaregion by both the U.S. and Canadian governments. Megaregions are defined as areas where "boundaries begin to blur, creating a new scale of geography." These areas have codependent economic systems, shared natural resources and ecosystems, an influx of entrepreneurial business and technology firms, and related population growth. They also share common transportation systems, including highways, rail lines, shipping lanes, and even a U.S./Canadian driver's license. **Welcome to our bioregion!**

Northern Cascades, Washington

Introduction

A Different Perspective

This Guide is written for a generation of high school students possessing a substantially different perspective on college and career options than prior generations. Media and tech-savvy, these students tend to be socially, culturally, and politically aware and active from their earliest high school years. They have strong opinions and make their voices heard.

Many high school students are questioning the value of a four year college education and are wary of taking on high levels of debt. Some of these students lack motivation for the college research and application process. Having struggled with the chaos of the COVID-19 shutdowns and the spotty success of virtual learning, they may have little enthusiasm for the stress of writing essays and meeting deadlines.

The search for self-identity is paramount in this generation. The prospect of being judged as worthy or unworthy of admission to a college by anonymous adults has little appeal. To counter this attitude, we have taken a different approach in designing our PNW Guide. We invite adventurous and curious high school students to explore and discover the Pacific Northwest region while offering the in-depth information that our current generation of high school students want and need as they begin to research options and opportunities for post-secondary education and training.

An Inclusive Readership Goal

Our purpose in producing this regional Guide is to support students, parents, counselors, and mentors as they research equitable access to, and inclusion in post-secondary education and training and to serve as a useful tool for clarifying students' options and opportunities beyond high school.

As experienced mentors and college counselors, we here at Navigations2College and the Oregon ASPIRE Volunteer program often work with aspiring high school students who face numerous challenges in enrolling in a residential four year college or university. We also know that a four year college degree is not the only pathway to a fulfilling career and financial stability.

In our work and in this PNW Guide, we encourage students to explore community college/university collaborations that can transfer credits into a four year degree program if desired, and we also make them aware of the many institutions that offer two year Associate degrees and short-term Certificate programs on their campuses.

In designing this Guide, however, we have chosen to focus on institutions with residential housing because we believe that all aspiring students should at least explore their options for an on-campus experience. We strive to help them understand where and what opportunities for experiential learning, research, fieldwork, community engagement, internships, and co-op experiences, and financial aid resources, might be available to them.

Profiles Plus

Our Guided Exploration is designed to inform and excite students about the wide range of college experiences and natural environments they can find within this astoundingly beautiful and ecologically fascinating Cascadian bioregion of North America.

In the following pages, you will find detailed **Profiles** of a selection of Pacific Northwest higher education institutions including private and public universities. Each profile describes the institution's **Location, Sense of Community, Academics, Student Life Experience, Financial Accessibility,** and **Study Away options.** Every profile is augmented by a **Data Chart** of essential statistical information for comparison and a **Highlight** discussion.

Multiple **IN FOCUS** sections expand coverage of the region's colleges and universities beyond those profiled. These informative sections provide samples of the wide variety of innovative and special-interest programs, tuition discounts, rare majors, and other valuable resources and amenities offered by our Pacific Northwest colleges and universities.

Guidance

Although this is not a how-to-apply-to-college book, it does introduce students and their families to critical initial steps in assessing their financial needs and options in an **In Focus** section on **Affordable and Equitable Access.**

We also include a short **Workshop on College Research and Comparison** designed to aid students in identifying the higher education institutions that most closely match their academic interests, social community, financial needs, environmental preferences, and potential career goals. **The Further Resources** Section provides links to valuable and current sources of reliable advice and information on all aspects of the college application process.

Navigate Your Path to Higher Education and Training by researching options, opportunities, and resources, and reflecting on your passions and preferences.

A College Research and Comparison Workshop

Why Do This?

This short series of exercises is based on the highly successful workshops for high school students designed by our Navigations2College counseling staff. Completing these exercises will save time and reduce the stress of indecision about what you want in a college experience.

These exercises will enable you to develop a viable list of colleges that best fit you. They will help you define your criteria for the type of community, range of academic programming, learning style options, recreational and residential life experiences, study away opportunities, and the level of affordability and accessibility you need and want.

Exercise A: Begin to Define Your Personal Criteria

From one of the three **PROFILES** sections, open any Profile at random, preferably one for an unfamiliar college. Read it carefully but totally ignore the location and financial aid sections, as those are not relevant at this beginning level of your research.

As you read that Profile make careful notes on what specific characteristics of Community, Academic, Recreational and Residential Life, and Study Away programs you immediately liked and also what aspects you would have absolutely no interest in. Be open to discovering features, programs, and options that you are not familiar with but that still sound interesting or exciting to you.

Now **randomly** choose at least **2** more **Profiles** to read, picking them from each of the other sections to compare. As before, try to pick colleges you know very little about so you are not prejudiced by prior knowledge, advertising, or hearsay from other students. Use what you read to add to your notes about your individual preferences.

Now refer to your notes and design a three-column **Preferences Chart** like this and **fill in the blanks:**

ABSOLUTES	STRONG PREFERENCES	BONUSES
My College absolutely must have these Features or Characteristics.	**These are Features or Characteristics I would strongly prefer to have at my college.**	**I would like my college to have these Features or Characteristics, but others are more important.**

Now save this working chart in a Navigations2College file where you can easily access it and edit it if necessary.

Exercise B: Exploring Your Interests and Passions

For this exercise, please make another three column chart with these headings and descriptions and **fill in the blanks**:

MY INTERESTS	MY HOBBIES	MY PASSION(S)
Things I am curious about, want to know more about, learn to do, or plan to get more involved in at college.	**Activities that I have dedicated effort to for a long period of time, just for pleasure and fun.**	**An activity, goal, or idea that I am intensely excited by and deeply absorbed in.**
Activities that I commit my time to when I have space, time, and motivation, but tend to be temporary involvements of time, or are seasonal activities.	**Something I do regularly for relaxation, self-fulfillment, and self-education, or training, which is not any kind of required schoolwork, job requirement, or social commitment.**	**Something I would have great difficulty living happily without.**
Things I have enjoyed being engaged with for a while and gave me the confidence to discover and explore other interests.		**Something that defines me or that I feel I was destined to learn, play, follow, or build.**
		Something I feel compelled to become good at, or develop expertise in, and may be linked to an innate talent, intellectual gift, or a strong personal characteristic.

Now save this working chart in a Navigations2College file where you can easily access it and edit it if necessary.

Exercise C: College Location and Financial Viability

Next, answer these questions for yourself:

- **Distance from home:** How far from home would I want my college to be?
- **Climate:** Will climate/weather be a deciding factor in my decision about a college?
- **Size:** How large is too large? How small is too small?
- **Faculty:** How important to me are small discussion classes and more direct engagement and support from faculty?
- **Access:** Is my high school academic achievement record strong enough to expect academic merit aid at this college?
- **Other Scholarships:** Would I qualify for any scholarships that reward talent, athletic skills, leadership, or significant volunteer experience?

NOTE:
You can use all your answers to fine tune your potential college list, but be open to discovering something new and exciting as you read the PROFILES and the IN FOCUS sections in this Guide. **Now is your time to be adventurous!**

Exercise D: Developing a College Comparison Chart

- Now you can combine your results from Exercises A, B, and C into a College Comparison Chart that you can begin to fill out as you study the Profiles and Data Charts in this Guide and from other sources.
- Then you can go to the websites of those colleges that interest you to do deeper research into the majors, programs, amenities, and accessibility of each institution and compare these to your personal criteria.

Here is an example:

College Name: ____________________ **Website:** ____________________

Location and Size Fit	Community Features I Like	Academic Programs of Interest	Recreational Activities of Interest	Residential and Social Life Features I Like	My Merit Aid Options Here	My Scholarship Options Here?

Making Contact/Showing Interest

Once you have identified a college that seems to come close to matching most of your criteria, it is time to make contact.

How to Contact an Admissions Office

The Home Page of each institution will have a link to "Admissions" or "Apply." Go there after you have studied the institution's website carefully and have a question and/or want to show your interest. Your contact with a counselor is not an application for admission. It is just a way to show your interest, get your questions answered, and to make sure you get placed on their 'potential applicant' list.

1. Find Your Regional Counselor.

Many colleges will have a designated counselor for your specific region of the country and even for different areas of your state. Often the first page of the Admissions section will have a "find your admissions counselor" or a "meet the admissions team" link. If so, then use that to identify your designated counselor and their direct email. If the college or university does not offer immediate access to your regional counselor then just use the admissions@...email address offered.

2. 'Contact Us' forms.

Many institutions will offer you a Contact or Interest form to fill out. This can place you on their e-mailing list and even get you a brochure or viewbook in the mail. Some contact forms are simple, just asking for basic personal information, name, birthdate, and addresses, when you expect to start college, and whether you would be entering as a first year or transfer student. Others want to know a lot more about your interests. Some will ask for your parents' addresses as well. A lot of the questions are optional, so choose wisely in order to control your mail. Move college info emails to a designated college research file so you don't lose them or have to spend time searching back for them. We recommend not offering to receive texts at first. These can quickly become overwhelming and annoying.

3. Writing to an Admissions Office or to a Counselor.

- Always begin your formal email to a counselor or admissions office as Dear ..., never Hi! or Hey there! If you do not have a counselor's name then just open with Dear Friends at...U., or Dear Admissions Staff....
- Begin by identifying yourself, your home location, high school, and current grade or graduation date. Be brief and to the point and make sure to proofread to correct spelling or grammar mistakes before hitting Send.
- State one or two specific reasons for your interest in the institution and its programs. Be honest and straight-forward and do not brag about yourself. Do not ask a question about something when the answer is easily found on their website. Otherwise they will know you have not bothered to study their website and will not have a good first impression of you as potentially good student.
- Use phrases such as "I would like to know..." "I am curious about...." "Would you please tell me..." "Could you advise me about ..."
- If you are likely to qualify for an Honors program or major merit aid scholarship do express your interest in it or any other special program or activity that appeals to you.
- End your email with a "Thank you for your time. Sincerely yours..."

How to Use this Guide

The Profiles of each selected college and university address the five most common questions our high school students ask.

Location: Where is this college/university? What is the climate like? What is there to do there?

Sense of Community: Is this a campus community that will not only make me feel welcomed and valued but that I could get excited about being actively involved in? Can I see myself loving it there? Will there be students from other states and countries studying there? How will I make friends?

Academics: Does this college offer a curriculum, majors and minors, and special programs and research options that will engage me, help me develop my interests, and build critical skills toward a successful future? What about class sizes? Is there a focus on experiential learning and options for career training like internships, a co-op program, and responsible community service opportunities?

Student Activities and Residential Life: What are the dorms like? Are they inclusive? Is the food service and selection good? What is there in the way of a social life? What kinds of extracurricular activities are offered at this institution?

Financial Aid: What level of financial aid and types of scholarships are offered, and to what kinds of students?

Study Away: Will I be stuck on campus for four years, or does this college offer well-developed programs for studying off-campus, abroad, or on exchange with another college?

Portland, Oregon with Mt. Hood in background.

SECTION ONE

Private Colleges

What are the Major Differences between Private and Public Colleges and Universities?

Class Sizes and Student to Faculty Ratios

Most classes at small private colleges and universities can have as few as 10-20 students. These are often held in a round table/seminar style that encourages discussion and cross-fertilization of ideas and viewpoints.

Professors at the smaller institutions can learn the names and faces of their students more easily, and the student to faculty ratio tends to be smaller, leading to more engagement between faculty and students, both in and out of class.

The larger institutions, whether public or private, tend to have larger class sizes, except in the Honors Colleges and other specialized learning programs that have smaller cohorts.

Diversity

Many PNW private colleges struggle to meet their diversity goals for racial, ethnic, cultural, and first-generation college student diversity. As a result, some have developed special programs and financial aid funds to attract and enroll such students.

Public institutions tend to enroll more students from their state and regional high schools and therefore closely reflect the population diversity of those communities.

Course and Program Availability

Many private colleges offer a surprising number of majors for their size. They often offer students more flexible options and more freedom to add minors, fit in a study abroad experience, or to choose interdisciplinary majors and/or independent study.

Why Choose a Private College?

- ✔ **Lower student to faculty ratio**
- ✔ **Smaller number of students**
- ✔ **More flexible major and minor options**
- ✔ **Regional diversity**
- ✔ **Generous merit and need-based scholarships**

At some of the larger public universities, it can be difficult to schedule all the required courses you need to graduate within four years, unless you home in on a major early on and stick very close to the recommended sequence of courses.

Fitting in a study abroad experience and or internships can also require very careful planning well in advance.

Cost of Attendance

Public colleges and universities draw part of their funding from their state governments. These public funds help keep in-state tuition for public universities much lower than that of private institutions. Nonetheless, the charges for room and board at our private and public universities are very similar.

The good news is that most private colleges offer generous merit and need-based scholarships that can make them more accessible and more affordable.

We encourage students to include private colleges in their research and comparison efforts as well as public universities. Remember that "sticker price" is unlikely to be the final offer to any student that the college or university wants to enroll.

Selected College Profiles
by State and Province

Alaska
- University of Alaska Fairbanks
- University of Alaska Anchorage
- University of Alaska Southeast
- Alaska Pacific University

British Columbia
- UBC-Okanagan
- Quest University
- Vancouver Island University

Washington
- Central Washington University
- Evergreen State College
- Gonzaga University
- Pacific Lutheran University
- University of Puget Sound
- Saint Martin's University
- Seattle University
- University of Washington
- Washington State University
- Western Washington University
- Whitman College

Oregon
- Lewis and Clark College
- Linfield University
- Oregon Institute of Technology
- University of Oregon
- Oregon State University (with OSU-Cascades)
- University of Portland
- Portland State University
- Reed College
- Southern Oregon University
- Willamette University (with Pacific Northwest College of the Arts)

Northern California
- Cal Poly Humboldt

Idaho
- Boise State University
- College of Idaho
- Lewis and Clark State College
- University of Idaho
- Idaho State University

Montana
- Carroll College
- University of Montana
- Montana State University
- Montana Technological Institute
- Montana Western University
- Salish Kootenai College

Residential Community Colleges Sample
- Bellevue College
- Central Oregon Community College
- Missoula College
- North Idaho College
- Prince William Sound College
- College of the Redwoods
- College of the Siskiyous
- Treasure Valley Community College

Alaska Pacific University

Anchorage, Alaska / www.alaskapacific.edu

Alaska Pacific University attracts adventurous students with strong interests in environmental, marine, and outdoor studies, and, like other ECO League colleges, APU focuses on experiential and place-based learning in all their academic departments.

Location

In this gateway to the Alaskan wilderness, Anchorage residents are familiar with moose wandering around their neighborhoods and bears as frequent visitors. This vibrant city of 290,000 is full of ambitious and adventurous young people who spend a lot of time working hard and enjoying outdoor recreational challenges.

Alaska Pacific University (APU) is situated on a 174 acre forested campus right in the city. It is adjacent to The University of Alaska campus, and shares amenities such as an extensive consortium library.

Anchorage has a milder climate than other cities in Alaska, but winter still brings the snow and cold expected at this latitude, which is similar to that of Oslo, Norway.

Community

APU attracts adventurous and curious students who are searching for a college experience far from the norm. The college offers an opportunity to live and study in a very small community with an unusually rich cultural, ethnic, and socio-economic mix of students and faculty, as well as experience Alaska's unique environment.

Out of state students constitute about seventeen percent of the student enrollment.

APU undergrad students enjoy a warm, tight-knit learning community with a faculty who know them individually and support their development, both as students and in their progress toward achieving their personal goals.

The campus adjoins that of the larger University of Alaska which offers opportunities to enrich and expand student social and cultural options, as well as add certain language courses.

Anchorage, AK Skyline

APU also offers community members and organizations a place to share their art, cultural heritage, talents, and passions. Community events are often held in APU's theater and gallery spaces and serve to bring the Anchorage community and students together.

Academics

The APU curricula in the **Sustainability Studies, Marine and Environmental Sciences,** and **Outdoor Studies** list of specialized majors emphasizes extensive and in-depth field studies and challenging expeditions in Alaska's formidable mountains and coastal waters, as well as traditional on-campus courses.

The same hands-on, active learning focus is evident in every other college department, from Health Sciences to Counseling Psychology to Teacher Education and the project–based learning curricula for Business Administration.

In addition, APU has an impressive experiential education resource in their nearby 800 acre **Kellogg Spring Creek Farm Learning Center.** This provides space for field research in resilient food systems, innovative renewable design, the building of organizational collaboration on sustainability research, as well as nature and place-based education.

To allow for periods of field study, in-depth research, and off-campus courses, each semester begins with the student's selection of a single course taught in an initial, intensive, four week block. This is followed by a twelve week session of study in several selected courses. The **Academic Block Calendar** allows students to focus on fewer subjects at a time and provides more opportunity for active learning and internships, a junior practicum, and research applications. The Block calendar also corresponds to the other **Eco League** colleges facilitating student exchanges between those colleges.

APU has a strategic affiliation with the Alaska Tribal Health Consortium, which offers opportunities for student/faculty research in healthcare and public health. APU faculty members are recognized scholars in snow science, fisheries, food systems, marine science, and other research relevant to the Circumpolar North.

APU is also a partner in **AK UNiTE**, a National Science Foundation supported network in Undergraduate Biology Education, which connects students to paid field research experiences.

Recreational Activities and Residential Life

In addition to multiple outdoor recreation options at different levels of physical challenge, APU has an impressive indoor climbing wall and a sports center with an indoor saltwater pool, weight room, and full size gym. **The Sports Center** adjoins the city's extensive trail system which includes several lighted trails for nighttime use by hikers, bikers, and skiers.

APU's **Nordic Ski Center** is a training ground for Olympic skiers and World Champions. The Center uses local trails and the **Thomas Training** Center on the Eagle Glacier which allows competitive cross country skiers access to good snow in all seasons. Competitive high school skiers can enroll in an **Early Honors Dual Credit program** and train here.

Student organizations include a range of clubs for those interested in everything from Aquatics to Alpine sports to Gaming and Hiking activities. Professionally focused organizations include an Environmental Public Health Club and the Student Nurses Association.

Students also publish and promote the **Turnagain Currents** student journal, which gives voice to members of the university community.

The **ASAPU Student Government Association** offers leadership and management experience as well. There are three student residence options and all first and second-year students who live further than sixty miles from campus are required to live on campus.

Dining is cafeteria style and incorporates sustainable local foods and organic products. There is a campus coffee shop and a weekly Farmers Market as well.

Financial Aid

APU offers many scholarships, including those for travel on expeditions, as well as merit based, and specific endowed scholarships. The APU **Promise Tuition Grant** is a need-based program that assists full-time undergraduates who are Pell eligible, by reducing or waiving the cost of tuition.

Study Away

APU is a member of the **Eco League of U.S. colleges,** which means its students can choose to spend up to two semesters studying at one or two of the other **Eco League Colleges** as exchange students and earning full credit toward their APU diplomas. Faculty members also lead **Global Research Expeditions.**

The EcoLeague Colleges

The EcoLeague is a consortium of liberal arts colleges dedicated to ecologically focused education and to modeling sustainability through their operations and facilities. While most consortia in the United States are grounded in geographic proximity, the EcoLeague consortium is grounded in a mission of bio-regional education for sustainability.

Sharing a mutual commitment to environmental and community health and sustainability, the Eco League Colleges are located in climates as varied as Arizona and Maine which means students on exchange get to study different ecosystems and varied community issues.

The EcoLeague consortium is currently comprised of six members:

Alaska Pacific University; College of the Atlantic; Dickinson College; New College of Florida; Northland College; and Prescott College.

Alaska Pacific University Basic Statistics

Undergraduate Enrollment	Freshman Class Enrollment	Institution Total Enrollment	Female/Male Student Ratio	Female/Male Faculty Ratio	Student/ Faculty Ratio
418	42	555	65/35	54/46	7/1
# of 1st Year Applications	**# of 1st Year Women Admitted**	**# of 1st Year Men Admitted**	**# of Transfer Students Admitted**	**Overall Yield**	**% of Out-of-State Students**
428	361	142	65	16%	17%
% Students Living in Campus Housing	**% Fraternity/ Sorority Participation**	**% Students Receiving Some Level of Financial Aid**	**1st Year Students Retention Rate**	**% Classes Under 30**	**% Caucasian/ White Faculty**
56%	0	84%	65%	100%	--
# Caucasian / White Students	**# Hispanic / Latinx Students**	**# Asian Students**	**# Black Students**	**# Native Alaskan /Amer., Hawaiian / Pacific Islander**	**% International Students**
189	50	22	11	133	6
In-State Tuition and Fees	**Room and Board**	**Out-of-State Tuition and Fees**	**Honors Program Cost**	**Honors Program Grant**	**Athletic Division**
$20,760	$8,330	$20,760	n/a	n/a	n/a

Notes:

Carroll College

Helena, Montana / www.carroll.edu

Carroll College is a robust private Catholic college offering highly regarded liberal arts and professional degrees and a very competitive athletics program that takes pride in its Scholar-Athletes.

Location

Helena is a small historic city of 34,000 and the Montana state capitol. Situated midway between Glacier and Yellowstone National Parks at an elevation of 4045ft., the area boasts seventy miles of trails for hiking and biking that begin right in town, as well as nearby lakes and rivers for water sports and fishing. A small ski area is nearby. The handsome 63 acre campus is just a few blocks from the busy downtown.

Helena is an economically stable city in which the workforce is primarily professionals, white collar workers. They tend to be employees of small businesses, state government agencies, or public administration offices. The city has a traditionally low unemployment rate and is predominately white.

The climate is semi-arid with low humidity. Winters are chilly and snowy, but with periods of welcome moderation due to the occasional warm western winds known as Chinooks.

Community

The strong sense of community and school spirit at Carroll is fostered by adherence to Catholic social teaching, which focuses on family, community, and participation, and by promoting the common good.

The College attracts over half of its eleven hundred students from out of state, primarily from Washington, Oregon, Idaho, California, and Colorado. Eighty-seven percent of students identify as white, while about fifty percent identify as either Catholic (37%) or Christian of other denominations (16%).

Carroll's high priorities are the physical, spiritual, and emotional health of its students and staff. There is no tolerance for drug use or keg parties on campus.

The College's **Hunthausen Center for Peace and Justice** provides community service opportunities of the students that strengthen the warm relationship between the city's residents and the College.

Helena, MT

Academics

Carroll College is known for rigorous academics in every department. The faculty are well-engaged in campus life and caring and supportive of their students but expect students' best efforts. The Biology programs, especially its interdisciplinary approach to biochemistry and molecular biology, stand out and are the most popular, followed by nursing and health sciences. Students report that the two-thirds of classes with twenty or fewer students are generally the most productive, while larger classes can be far less engaging.

The College's inspired **Anthrozoology** major is growing in popularity and drawing more students from out of state. It explores human-animal interactions in a cross-disciplinary program applicable to veterinary medicine, animal assisted therapies, canine training, and humane education. The program also offers hands-on experience and research projects with small animals, horses, and wildlife, at a training center right on campus.

The College offers several majors that focus on the environment from different perspectives, including engineering, science, management and policy, and outreach and interpretation. Field trips such as a two-week immersion in Winter Ecology at Yellowstone National Park and an experiential and interdisciplinary course that begins with a weeklong trip on the Missouri river are typical of the faculty's imaginative use of this region's wealth of opportunity for intensive environmental studies.

The renowned **McLaughlin Research Institute for Biomedical Sciences** offers research internships for Carroll students. The **Hunthausen Center for Peace and Justice** is an affiliate of the global Catholic Relief Services organization, which focuses on confronting world-wide poverty and inequality.

The three-year **Honors Scholars** program offers a Great Books and seminar-based curricula for a small cohort of aspiring students who desire flexibility in shaping discussions and engaging in active inquiry. Most Honors seminars count as a CORE requirement, and students in any major can participate.

Recreational Activities and Residential Life

First and second-year students are required to live on campus. There is a mix of residences, including standard dormitories, a quaint historic building, and unfurnished campus apartments to rent for older students. One dorm allows students in the canine training program to have their trainee dogs live with them. Another, known as the quiet dorm, has single rooms with sinks, with one communally shared bathroom on each floor. Student reviews of the food served on campus suggest improvement in quality and selection variety is overdue.

There is an abundance of clubs and organizations to join. These include **Collar Scholars**, a group that raises puppies to be service dogs, a Gay/Straight Alliance, and many outdoor sports-related, academic and professional interest groups, and political, social action, and community service organizations.

The relatively new and impressive campus activity center provides everything you need for fitness and recreation, intramural sports, and space for socializing and studying. Discounted passes for the nearby four-star rated city golf course and the small Great Divide ski area 23 miles up the mountain are available to students.

Athletics at Carroll are a draw for competitive athletes, and the college is known for fostering integrity, character, and sportsmanship and for the academic achievements of its athletes. Fielding seven men's and eight women's NAIA teams at this small college means many students play a sport or two. With many alumni living in the city, home games often draw good crowds, especially for football, which boasts six national championships.

Financial Aid

Carroll College offers institutional merit, activity, and athletic scholarships. The College gives institutional grants or scholarships to about 99% of incoming students, but Carroll scholarships are reduced if students move off campus. There are Montana **Advantage** grants for students from Montana, plus a number of other scholarships.

Study Away

As a **Catholic Relief Services Global** campus, Carroll encourages students to explore community-engaged service abroad programs. The College also sponsors a variety of faculty-led courses that take students off-campus for study and fieldwork, both in the U.S. and abroad, as well as international student exchange programs.

Catholic Relief Services (CRS)

The mission of CRS is to assist impoverished and disadvantaged people overseas, working in the spirit of Catholic social teaching to promote the sacredness of human life and the dignity of the human person.

Colleges and Universities such as Carroll collaborate with CRS by becoming a CRS Global Campus. The benefits include leadership and advocacy training, professional development, participation in academic symposia, and joint speaking engagements on campus.

Although their mission is rooted in the Catholic faith, CRS operations serve people based solely on need, regardless of race, religion, or ethnicity.

CRS trains on-campus chapters of student leaders to mobilize their peers, and bring to life the mission of global solidarity on campus. Chapters are connected to each other, and to CRS, in order to build a national movement for impactful change.

Carroll College Basic Statistics

Undergraduate Enrollment	Freshman Class Enrollment	Institution Total Enrollment	Female/Male Student Ratio	Female/Male Faculty Ratio	Student/ Faculty Ratio
1098	280	1121	61/39	54/46	11/1
# of 1st Year Applications	**# of 1st Year Women Admitted**	**# of 1st Year Men Admitted**	**# of Transfer Students Admitted**	**Overall Yield**	**% of Out-of-State Students**
1499	757	501	98	22%	55%
% Students Living in Campus Housing	**% Fraternity/ Sorority Participation**	**% Students Receiving Some Level of Financial Aid**	**1st Year Students Retention Rate**	**% Classes Under 30**	**% Caucasian/ White Faculty**
87%	0%	57%	80%	91%	57%
# Caucasian / White Students	**# Hispanic / Latinx Students**	**# Asian Students**	**#Black Students**	**# American Indian/ Alaskan, Hawaiian Native Pacific Islander**	**#International Students**
80%	4%	1%	1%	1%	2%
In-State Tuition and Fees	**Room and Board**	**Out-of-State Tuition and Fees**	**Honors Program Cost**	**Honors Program Grant**	**Athletic Division**
$38,106	$10,416	$38,106	0	n/a	NAIA

Notes:

Gonzaga University

Spokane, Washington / www.gonzaga.edu

Community spirit, community service, and community cohesiveness are the touchpoints of this medium-sized Jesuit Catholic university noted for its rigorous academics and legendary basketball success stories.

Location

Spokane is the major urban center of inland Washington State and a gateway to the Palouse, one of the most scenic and unique agricultural areas in the world, with its rolling hills, highly productive wheat and legume fields, and famous vineyards. Over 223,000 city residents enjoy a four season climate with 200 days of sunshine, five ski areas within an hour and a half, and abundant lakes. The region's numerous trails include 35 miles of paved bike trails.

Spokane has a reinvigorated downtown full of shops, galleries, restaurants, theaters, breweries, dance clubs, and cozy bars. Close to several national forests in the surrounding mountain ranges, the area can suffer smoke pollution during the summer wildfire season.

The city has begun attracting tech refugees and entrepreneurs from larger cities, bringing greater diversity to the area's demographics. Five major airlines service the Spokane International Airport.

Community

Gonzaga's long and deep commitment to Spokane is demonstrated in many community service programs and projects for which the nearly 5000 undergraduates eagerly volunteer. The **Center for Community Engagement** is well-staffed, runs extensive youth programs in the city's public schools, and collaborates with community organizations.

The 152 acre campus also offers many meeting and study spaces that encourage mixing and studying together. Students speak warmly of their supportive faculty and their open door office hours.

The University encourages exploration across academic genres, perspectives, and divergent ideas and welcomes students from all beliefs and backgrounds. About half the faculty and forty percent of the students are Catholic. The University struggles to reach greater diversity in the student and faculty populations. More than fifty percent of students come from out of state, with many coming from California and Oregon.

Academics

The preponderance of small classes at an undergraduate institution of this size makes Gonzaga stand out, as does the challenging selection of required core courses. These introduce students to the full breadth of a traditional Jesuit liberal arts curriculum, including courses in the fields of religion and philosophy. Attendance is required in most classes, and professors do not inflate grades. The University promotes high standards of conduct and conflict resolution. The Gonzaga Institute for Hate Studies and the Center for Cura Personalis offer support and guidance in these areas.

Students earn their good grades through hard work, but the course load is generally manageable, and the education here is geared toward developing the whole person. Class participation is expected, professors know their students' names, and faculty members, not T.A.s., teach all classes.

Global learning is valued at Gonzaga and the University has a yearlong program at their site in Florence, Italy that gives students a full year of credits. STEM students say that weaker students in their fields are weeded out early, ensuring a stronger group of students moves into the more advanced courses.

Business programs at Gonzaga are the most popular, followed by engineering, social sciences, and biology. Gonzaga also has a well-regarded nursing program and a reputation for getting students into medical school. The departments of communication, journalism, and psychology also get high praise from students. The Gonzaga Debate Institute supports competitive Debate teams.

The Honors Program focuses on social justice, global awareness, and an interdisciplinary perspective on issues and problem solving. Honors students can take extra credit courses without any extra charge so there is flexibility for a double major, or for additional concentrations. The Center for Undergraduate Research and Creative Inquiry facilitates, funds, and supports student projects and presentations through various fellowships, research assistantships, and Scholars programs.

Recreational Activities and Residential Life

First and second year students are required to live on campus, with options from traditional dorm living to themed ones that puts together students with common interests. The **Learns2Lead** floor, for instance, trains first year students for roles such as resident assistants, student body officials, camp coordinators, and community leaders. A different dorm houses first and second year students interested in sustainable outdoor activities and promotes many outdoor programs.

On-campus residents have a choice of meal plans and some dorms have ample kitchen facilities. First year Honors students can live in an Honors Living/Learning Community By junior year, however, a substantial number of students find off-campus housing with friends, in group houses, or rent apartments in a nearby university-owned complex. What hard-partying exists at Gonzaga is usually found at off-campus venues.

The **Center for Student Involvement** is home to more than 110 clubs and organizations, including the **Gonzaga Outdoors** programs and the **Payne Center for Leadership Development.** Students manage a radio station and create student publications such as **Gonzaga Magazine, Our Voices Journal,** and the **One World Journal**. Students passionately support Gonzaga's Division I sports teams and the University is proud of their scholar-athletes' strong academic and volunteer work.

Financial Aid

98% of incoming students receive merit, or grant, aid, and about 200 students receive athletic scholarships. The University is committed to supporting undocumented students as part of its faith-inspired commitment to diversity and inclusion.

Study Away

Gonzaga's ultimate offering in study away is the **Gonzaga in Florence** program in the **Mozilo Center.** With an emphasis on being a safe way to study abroad, the Center offers a broad range of courses, activities, and opportunities for internships and community service. Participants can live with host families or at a family-owned hotel and prepare beforehand by participating in a **Florence Scholars** language and cultural studies program. Gonzaga has a full range of other vetted programs for studies abroad.

Student Support Services at Colleges and Universities

The American College Health Association provides comprehensive data on the health of college students. The 2021 ACHA survey indicates that 46.8% of the 33,204 college students surveyed feel that student health and well-being is a priority of their college/university. About one-third reported that they had received either psychological or mental health services within the past year. Of those, over 43% had received that assistance at their campus health or counseling center. The top four problems that students reported as having negatively impacted their academic performance were procrastination, issues with a faculty member, hazing, and the death of someone dear to them.

The **Gonzaga Center for Cura Personalis (CCP)** is one of many campus programs designed to support students. It is dedicated to providing a caring and seamless learning experience for each student. "Cura personalis" means care for the whole person and Gonzaga does this through mentoring and support of any students who are dealing with challenges of mind, body, or spirit. The CCP staff members do not provide clinical therapy. They do connect students with the resources they need and work collaboratively across the institution to develop support plans that promote self-advocacy, empower students to navigate toward their own solutions, and help them shape their own lives. Gonzaga faculty and staff are encouraged to refer students of concern to the Center so they can get the holistic support they need to feel cared for, supported, and valued.

Gonzaga University Basic Statistics

Undergraduate Enrollment	Freshman Class Enrollment	Institution Total Enrollment	Female/Male Student Ratio	Female/Male Faculty Ratio	Student/ Faculty Ratio
4986	1311	7381	58/42	49/51	11/1
# of 1st Year Applications	**# of 1st Year Women Admitted**	**# of 1st Year Men Admitted**	**# of Transfer Students Admitted**	**Overall Yield**	**% of Out-of-State Students**
8853	3706	2036	285	19%	52%
% Students Living in Campus Housing	**% Fraternity/ Sorority Participation**	**% Students Receiving Some Level of Financial Aid**	**1st Year Students Retention Rate**	**% Classes Under 30**	**% Caucasian/ White Faculty**
53%	0%	48%	92%	81%	9%
# Caucasian / White Students	**# Hispanic / Latinx Students**	**# Asian Students**	**# Black Students**	**# American Indian/ Alaskan, Hawaiian Native Pacific Islander**	**# International Students**
3377	611	316	56	38	105
In-State Tuition and Fees	**Room and Board**	**Out-of-State Tuition and Fees**	**Honors Program Cost**	**Honors Program Grant**	**Athletic Division**
$50,735	$13,794	$50,735	0	$1800 per year	NAIA Div. I

Notes:

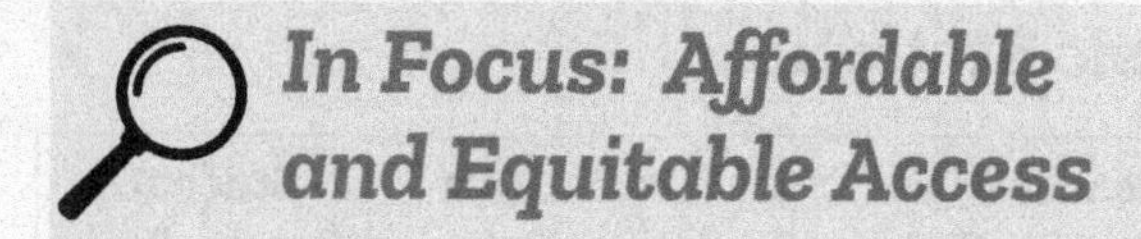

In Focus: Affordable and Equitable Access

Key Facts

Colleges and Universities use data from the **FAFSA** *(Free Application for Federal Financial Aid)* as a base for their decisions on how much financial aid they will offer to a student each year.

Financial Aid Packages will vary from institution to institution.

The size of discount a specific higher education institution can afford to offer an accepted student depends on the depth of the institution's financial resources. This is why all colleges and universities will assist their accepted students in accessing all federal financial aid programs for which they qualify, including Federal Grants and Federal Student Loans. They know that these resources can make the difference in whether an accepted student will enroll or not. The colleges also take a small handlers fee out of the grant for administration of those grants.

STEP ONE: Family Financial Assessment

Your Initial Assessment:

Families need to have a frank and open discussion about their income, assets, and debts with their college-aspiring teenager.* You will need a current financial aid estimate to do this. Here are the first steps:

]* **We recommend *The College Conversation* by Steinberg and Furda for its sensitive and practical advice to parents of college aspiring teens. (see *Further Resources Recommended Reading*)**

Use an estimating tool such as the

College Board's Estimated Financial Need Calculator *or the* **Federal Student Aid Estimator**

Here are the links to these estimator tools

https://studentaid.gov/aid-estimator
https://bigfuture.collegeboard.org/pay-for-college/paying-your-share/expected-family-contribution-calculator.

In preparation for using one or both of these estimators, parents will need access to their **Tax Return Documents.**

Federal Student Aid

Estimate Your Federal Student Aid

Our *Federal Student Aid Estimator* provides an estimate of what federal student aid you may be eligible to receive. To apply for financial aid, complete the *Free Application for Federal Student Aid* (FAFSA®) form.

Make sure to use data from the year specified by the estimator.

The student's income will also be counted, so if they earned enough to file a tax return, they will also need to report that income.

Follow the directions carefully and use the help links available to complete the estimator and receive the **Student Aid Index (SAI)** *(SAI is the new name for the EFC as of Fall 2022)*

Pell Grant: If the student qualifies for a **Pell Grant** or other federal student assistance, then that information will be provided in the SAI response along with details about any Federal Loans that they can take.

STEP TWO: Individual Assessment for Institutional Grants and Scholarships

Many factors can increase a college's interest in accepting a specific applicant and influence their willingness to award a merit scholarship or grant. Most colleges now make test scores optional. Most also use a holistic assessment of each applicant to ensure they consider not only academic achievement but many other valuable attributes. GPA remains the most influential factor in awarding merit aid but by no means the only one.

1. GPA A 3.5 GPA can initiate an academic merit award at many colleges and universities; the higher the GPA, the higher the offer may be. 3.0 is often the lowest to get a merit award, but there can be exceptions.

2. TALENTS in music, art, theater, dance, and even sports, if combined with an acceptable GPA, can be the basis for talent scholarships at many institutions.

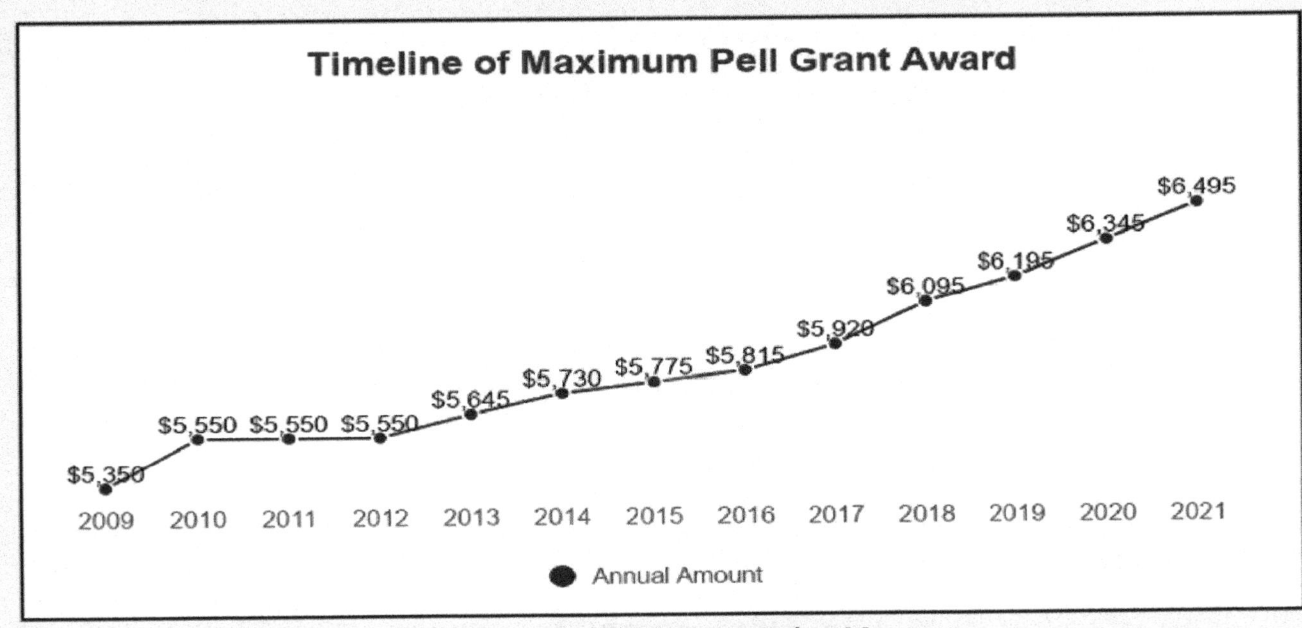

The maximum Federal Pell Grant for the 2022–23 award year has been increased to $6,895.
https://educationdata.org/pell-grant-statistics

3. COMPETITIVE TEAM PERFORMANCE Some colleges offer scholarships for applicants competitive in debate, robotics, and other team activities that the college supports.

4. LEADERSHIP AND COMMUNITY SERVICE Many institutions award scholarships to students with exceptional leadership skills and experience in school and community service.

5. DIVERSITY Most colleges and universities in the Pacific Northwest are eager to increase their student population's racial, socio-economic, and ethnic diversity. Many offer specific programs to attract and support diverse students and provide specific financial aid to attract them.

College Savings Accounts should be held in the parents' names, not the student's because the estimator tools will assume student-held savings accounts are available for college expenses and estimate accordingly.

See **Further Resources** for information about **529 investment accounts for college expenses.**

Note:

Students should never assess themselves, nor be assessed by others, solely on the basis of academic grades, but rather on where their strongest interest, highest energy, and heaviest time commitments are persistently and successfully directed.

Most college applications offer students an opportunity to fill out an activities list, answer questions, and write essays to highlight their strengths, talents, and personal story, and many will review portfolios and consider other additional evidence of potential.

See **Further Resources** for links to additional government financial aid programs.

Courtesy of Dave Coverly/SpeedBump.com

College of Idaho

Caldwell, Idaho /www.collegeof Idaho.edu

College of Idaho is known for its sense of community and unique PEAKS curriculum. PEAKS lets students explore, and then design their own curriculum, while achieving a practical, experience-rich, and career focused education.

Location

The College of Idaho campus is within the metropolitan area of Boise, Idaho, the third largest city in the Pacific Northwest and the state capitol. The small city of Caldwell lies just west of Boise at an elevation of 2375 ft., in a rich and scenic agricultural area called **Treasure Valley,** with ranches, farms, and vineyards surrounded by three mountain ranges.

The area, with its easy access to the canyons of the famous Snake River, 133 miles of trails, and abundant parks and forests, is a major destination for outdoor enthusiasts. The four season climate boasts 211 days of sun and about 8 inches of snow a year. Winter daytime temps dip into the low 40s only in Dec. and Jan.

Snake River, ID

With Boise just 30 minutes down the road, there is no lack of big city experience when students want it. Boise is rapidly becoming a new Silicon Valley-type tech center and offers myriad internship opportunities.

Community

Noted for high scores in social mobility and diversity, the C of I community of about eleven hundred students provides a variety of academics, sports, and off-campus opportunities rare for an institution of its size. Faculty members are easily accessible, and students are reputed to be among the happiest in the nation.

An **Honor Code** helps protect both personal freedom and community standards, and the College provides leadership skills-building opportunities for students. The well-endowed **Student Philanthropy Council** assumes all responsibility for awarding grants to local community service organizations, and students are trained to take on roles as **Involvement Coaches.** The Coaches encourage student participation in clubs, organizations, and sports activities and advise students on how to balance these activities with their academic commitments.

The College's **Advocate Center** is staffed by extensively trained students who act as first responders to students who are in need of supportive resources. This emphasis on communal responsibility inspires a sense of mutual care and shared mission among students, staff, and faculty. The College has earned distinction as a top college for social mobility. About 30% of students come from out of state and 60% of undergraduates live on campus.

Academics

The **PEAK Curriculum** is uniquely designed to develop professional, ethical, articulate, and knowledgeable graduates ready for the challenges ahead. C of I believes that students need to explore, discover, and develop a toolbox of skills to be prepared for an unpredictable future job market and new opportunities. Students explore and then choose one major and three minors, instead of just ticking off a general education list of required courses. This encourages competence development across several fields of interest.

High Impact Practice is the College's path to deep student engagement, whether through collaborative research with a faculty member, leadership and stewardship opportunities, field-based experiential learning through internships, work or service learning, or intensive faculty-led off campus programs.

The College's facilities include a Museum of Natural History, a Planetarium, a stunning new library, the Langroise Center for the Performing and Fine Arts, the 5000 seat Simplot Stadium for football, soccer, and lacrosse games and the 900 seat Jewett Auditorium for concerts, theatrical performances, and special events, along with several campus buildings listed on the National Register of Historic Places.

Business, Health Professions, Biological Sciences, and Psychology are the most popular majors, followed by the Social Sciences and Visual and Performing Arts. Students can also complete two additional specializations in a wide range of professional areas such as Finance, Book Arts, Coaching, and Data Science.

C of I takes pride in its Scholar-Athletes' records of excellent academic, as well as on-field performance and recent graduates include recipients of Rhodes, Marshall, Truman, and Goldwater post-graduate scholarships.

Recreational Activities and Residential Life

College of Idaho students are required to live in campus housing for six semesters. The seven residence halls offer a range of room sizes and bathroom facilities. Juniors and seniors can choose to live more independently in an apartment complex or in one of several neighborhood houses the College owns.

The elected **Student Government** leaders are responsible for ensuring campus life is vibrant, full of options, and inclusive. Clubs and organizations offer everything from identity-based groups to dance teams, honor societies, pre-professional interest organizations, and special interest clubs. Greek life consists of three national fraternities and three national sororities and one local sorority. There are also indoor and outdoor recreation clubs and the student-led **Outdoor Program.**

With a solid record of championships, C of I college athletes compete in the Cascade and Frontier Conferences at the Division II level in ten sports. The College also competes successfully at the national level with the United States Collegiate Ski and Snowboard Association teams.

Financial Aid

College of Idaho offers incoming students need-based aid, merit, and talent scholarships. The competitive **Heritage Scholarship** offers full tuition to a few exceptional students. Athletes can apply for **Athletic Talent Scholarships.** The **Kathryn Albertson Scholarship Competition** is another opportunity for funding.

Study Away

Faculty-led expeditions are popular at C of I and can take students as far away as Argentina or as close as Idaho's mountains for a four week **Winter Wilderness** expedition. Students can participate in affiliated international student abroad programs and Semester at Sea. There are grants for study abroad.

The College also collaborates with the **Verto Education Gap Year** program that earns transferable college credit while providing global cultural immersion options.

VERTO Education Gap Year

The innovative VERTO study abroad college experience is available to academically qualified applicants and includes full college credit for your first semester or first year of college at participating colleges and universities.

This credit transfers directly only to colleges that have joined a consortium of 60+ colleges and universities including the following five Pacific Northwest institutions; **The College of Idaho, College of the Siskiyous, Portland State University, Pacific Lutheran University, and Seattle University.**

If you are accepted at one or more of these institutions you can take advantage of the VERTO study abroad program for your first year or first semester of study. If you do VERTO for a full year you can choose two different locations in which to study. Verto offers a limited number of opportunity grants for students with financial need but participants cannot utilize federal education loans or grants and airfare to locations is not covered by these grants.

Study locations include England, Spain, Italy, the Czech Republic, Argentina, and Ireland.

The Verto application is similar to the Common Application and applicants must have a 2.5 GPA or above to be considered. It also requires a writing sample and a high school transcript. Seats are limited.

College of Idaho Basic Statistics

Undergraduate Enrollment	Freshman Class Enrollment	Institution Total Enrollment	Female/Male Student Ratio	Female/Male Faculty Ratio	Student/ Faculty Ratio
1,110	306	1,129	51/49	--	11/1
# of 1st Year Applications	**# of 1st Year Women Admitted**	**# of 1st Year Men Admitted**	**# of Transfer Students Admitted**	**Overall Yield**	**% of Out-of-State Students**
--	--	--	--	--	42%
% Students Living in Campus Housing	**Fraternity/ Sorority Participation**	**% Students Receiving Need-based Aid**	**1st Year Students Retention Rate**	**% Classes Under 30**	**% Caucasian/ White Faculty**
61%	Yes%	--	78.1%%	57%	--
# Caucasian / White Students	**% Hispanic / Latinx Students**	**# Asian Students**	**# Black Students**	**# American Indian/ Alaskan, Hawaiian /Native Pacific Islander**	**# International Students**
626	150	26	15	13	208
In-State Tuition and Fees	**Room and Board**	**Out-of-State Tuition and Fees**	**Honors Program Cost**	**Honors Program Grant**	**Athletic Division**
$34,680	$12,850	$34,680	n/a	varies	NAIA

Notes:

Lewis and Clark College

Portland, Oregon / www. lclark.edu

Lewis and Clark College offers big city life, coastal and mountain access, strong academics, and a welcoming environment at a beautiful campus while encouraging student voices, community action, and global perspectives.

Location

Portland, population 645,000, is one of the greenest cities in the U.S., not only in the amount of open space devoted to its 279 parks but also in its environmental consciousness and social activism. Located close to both the Pacific Ocean coast and the rugged Cascade Mountains range, Portland is highly walkable and noted for unique neighborhoods that are fun to explore, including a thriving twelve block **Culture District.**

Riverfront Park and Broadway Bridge, Portland OR

Portland's International airport and the expansive city transportation system are both outstanding. Like many cities, there is a noticeable homeless problem.Workplaces are casual and laid back, and most people cope well with Portland's weather, which in Jan-March can be grey and rainy, in contrast to the quite nice weather in other seasons.

Community

Community commitment to environmental sustainability is apparent on the beautiful and serene 137 acre forested Lewis and Clark campus, where wind power provides 100% of the College's electricity. The campus adjoins a large natural forest area in the city. The close-knit college community spirit is supported by co-curricular learning within residence halls that serve as Living/Learning Communities engaging students and faculty in co-curricular activities.

The **Center for Social Change and Community Involvement** connects students to city programs through its integrated approach to volunteer service learning opportunities, leadership development, and creative options for alternative spring break and immersion programs focused on creating positive social change through civic action.

The college's **Great Expectations** program reaches out to first generation and minority students with retreats and a mentorship program. Current renovation of the campus **Student Center** was designed with significant input from students. It will enhance campus life by providing additional open spaces, outdoor dining, and accessibility to gathering and meeting spaces.

Like most PNW colleges, Lewis and Clark is working to improve student and faculty diversity. Students comment on the college community's openness, acceptance of differences, eager engagement in college activities, service projects, and the plentiful and varied study abroad programs.

Academics

Students speak highly of the quality of teaching and good faculty engagement and availability. For a small college, the liberal arts curriculum offers an unusually wide choice of courses that satisfy core requirements. However, class size limits can make some very popular courses hard to get into.

Because the College also has exceptional mission-driven graduate schools of law, education, and counseling, there are clear pathways to those and other graduate programs. Some graduate programs are doable with only one more year of study; (4+1), such as the counseling program. Academic support services are easily accessible, and if, for some reason, you need more than four years to complete a very ambitious degree program, the College will cover an extra semester of tuition.

The College also offers a unique opportunity to study two languages within the **World Languages** major.

The theater and visual arts programs focus on developing artist-scholars. The music program supports unusual small ensembles such as Zimbabwean and Indian music, choir, orchestra, and an opera and musical theater workshop.

A **Connect-Portland** designation on a course means it is experiential, experimental, or inquiry-based learning that relates directly to the PNW region and to the city and often includes field work or other off-campus learning adventures.

Recreational Activities and Residential Life

The student-driven **College Outdoors** program is comprehensive, offering day, weekend, fall and spring-break trips, leadership opportunities, and wilderness trainings.

Students can participate in student organizations, affinity groups, and student-run events, and contribute to seven student-published journals or the bi-weekly Pioneer Log newspaper. Students staff and manage the college radio station and programs. There are also numerous campus events, including a three day **Gender Studies Symposium** which has been produced annually by L and C students and faculty for over forty years, and the **Ray Warren Symposium on Race and Ethnic Studies.** These bring distinguished guest speakers and workshop leaders from around the work to campus.

The college attracts many scholar-athletes who compete in ten men's and ten women's varsity sports in the NCAA Div. III athletic program. Club sports, including men's soccer and cycling, are also popular, and some compete in local leagues.

Students must live on campus for four semesters. There are nine residence halls, almost all of which are gender inclusive. Several dorms have been remodeled and renovated recently. There is also a relatively new dorm with LEED Gold environmental sustainability certification, as well as apartments for older students. Getting into the city proper is easy with a free shuttle that goes every hour from campus to downtown Portland and back.

Financial Aid

Lewis and Clark offers scholarships such as the Trustee, President's, Dean's, Faculty Scholarship, and Pioneer Award to top first year and transfer students, based on their academic program and performance. The College's most generous merit scholarship provides $50,000 annually to five students from NW Oregon and SW Washington.

Study Away

International education forms an integral part of the Lewis and Clark experience, and Global Perspectives courses are included in the general education requirements for graduation. Over 60% of students participate in the College's **Overseas Study** programs. To join these programs, students must have completed certain CORE course requirements and any required language in preparation. Faculty members often lead overseas and off-campus credit courses. Most faculty-led Regional Study overseas programs for academic credit are limited to a cohort of 25 students.

COLLEGE SYMPOSIUMS

A college symposium engages students in planning and managing a significant event to explore a particular topic or issue in-depth, and from different perspectives. It brings experts to campus to be presenters and speakers, to lead workshops, to participate in panel discussions, and to discuss their research and activities.

Symposiums also give students an opportunity to present their own research to an audience and to hear new ideas and different approaches to important issues and problems.

For the **41st Annual Gender Studies Symposium** at Lewis and Clark, the Symposium's student organizers asked participants to consider the ways fantasy allows us to produce material change and pursue "impossible" futures. They also urged exploration into how fantasy can be not only an act of personal imagination, but also a powerful form of political resistance.

Lewis and Clark's **18th Ray Warren Symposium on Race and Ethnic Studies** engaged participants in considering how we might understand and communicate the experiences of BIPOC individuals without relying so heavily on narratives of pain as we fight for justice. It asked whether joy can move us beyond burnout and fatigue and toward new spaces for love, strength, and perseverance.

Lewis and Clark College Basic Statistics

Undergraduate Enrollment	Freshman Class Enrollment	Institution Total Enrollment	Female/Male Student Ratio	Female/Male Faculty Ratio	Student/ Faculty Ratio
2,126	677	3,513	67/33	58/42	12/1
# of 1st Year Applications	**# of 1st Year Women Admitted**	**# of 1st Year Men Admitted**	**# of Transfer Students Admitted**	**Overall Yield**	**% of Out-of-State Students**
5,519	2938	1,447	107	15%	86%
% Students Living in Campus Housing	**Fraternity/ Sorority Participation**	**% Students Receiving Need-based Aid**	**1st Year Students Retention Rate**	**% Classes Under 30**	**% Caucasian/ White Faculty**
71%	n/a	60%	86.3%	86%	77%
# Caucasian / White Students	**% Hispanic / Latinx Students**	**# Asian Students**	**# Black Students**	**# American Indian/ Alaskan, Hawaiian /Native Pacific Islander**	**# International Students**
1,402	256	99	47	5	107
In-State Tuition and Fees	**Room and Board**	**Out-of-State Tuition and Fees**	**Honors Program Cost**	**Honors Program Grant**	**Athletic Division**
$57,584	$13,946	$57,584	n/a	n/a	NCAA Div.III

Notes:

Linfield University

McMinnville, Oregon / www. linfield.edu

This historic institution offers a supportive faculty and innovative learning environment for exploring interests and developing a solid career path. It also attracts students who want to continue to play their high school sport and those already seriously focused on a health profession.

Location

McMinnville is a lively city of 35,000 located on the Yamhill River in Oregon's famous wine country and less than an hour from both Portland and the Pacific Coast beaches. Noted for charming historic architecture and pedestrian friendly downtown shopping and dining, it is also home to six craft breweries, many wineries, a vibrant farmers market, and a notable Aviation and Space Museum.

The region's Mediterranean climate, with its warm summers and relatively mild but somewhat rainy winters, is ideal for winegrowers. A famous **International Pinot Noir Celebration** is held annually on the Linfield University Campus. There is good bus transportation to the coast and to metro Portland, as well within McMinnville itself.

Wine Science Training, Oregon

Community

The Linfield community of almost 1400 undergraduates attracts students mainly from Oregon and Washington, but also Hawaii and California, and has a solid representation of Latinix and mixed heritage students. The campus has some historic buildings dating from when the College was founded in the mid-1800s.

The award-winning **Linfield First Scholars** program provides mentorship and support to first generation college students, who make up nearly a third of the university's student population. Students attest to the tight-knit sense of community on campus and a feeling of a home away from home.

Because Linfield's strong athletic teams compete successfully at national and conference levels, many students come to Linfield seeking not only a career-focused college degree, but also a chance to continue to compete seriously in their team sport or sports. Student reviews consistently mention Linfield's caring and engaged faculty as perhaps its best asset with dining hall food as maybe the most problematic. They list the small class sizes, the inviting campus, and a warm, almost family-like social atmosphere, as reasons to love this small university.

Academics

Considered one of the best value colleges in Oregon, Linfield's Business, Education, Social Sciences, and Biology and Pre-nursing programs are the most popular majors. 25% of students major in one of the interdisciplinary Business School programs. Sports Management is a popular concentration in which students can focus on marketing, administration, coaching, broadcasting, and even the sports apparel business. It includes internships in the region's major sports companies.

Linfield is one of only a few PNW institutions offering an undergraduate degree in the wine business, production, and/or science. The **Evenstad Center for Wine Education** offers integrated and experiential courses and students are winning top prizes in **Intercollegiate Wine Business** competitions.

In 2021 Linfield's highly regarded **School of Nursing** expanded into a new twenty acre campus in northwest Portland, dramatically increasing teaching spaces and capacity of simulation suites and labs for this comprehensive school of nursing, which also offers an MSN in Leadership in Healthcare Ecosystems.

Linfield has innovative core education requirements that focus on student reflection about Ultimate Questions such as assumptions and beliefs, how the past affects the present, and how global and U.S. pluralism and diversity affect individuals and society.

The popular 4-1-4 academic calendar gives students a welcome January Term in which they can concentrate on a single course in greater depth, do research or an internship immersion, or choose to study either off-campus or abroad. Visual and performing arts and communication studies are part of the fabric of the university, and student participation is enthusiastic.

Student Activities and Residential Life

The Kiwanis Club-affiliated Circle K International, a student-led organization, develops opportunities for community service, leadership, and community fellowship. There are abundant clubs, a student run radio station, a newspaper, and even Podcast blogging facilities.

The **Linfield Lively Arts Series** brings top artists and ensembles to campus for performances, and the Music Department presents fun **Noontime Concerts** every week. There are also regular student performing arts recitals and theatrical productions to participate in and enjoy and multiple special interest clubs.

A new **Outdoor Recreation** program takes advantage of the university's prime outdoor exploration and adventure location. It offers a **Wilderness Immersion and Leadership Development (WILD)** pre-orientation program for incoming students. In the Northwest Conference at Division III Varsity athletes compete in ten men's and eleven women's sports, including swimming, tennis, and golf.

Fifteen residence halls include some that are pet-friendly, others that are substance-free, and both gender inclusive and single gender residence options are available. Apartment complexes are popular options for those in their junior year or above.

Greek life attracts about 30% of the student. Members sponsor service projects and social gatherings, but alcohol and drug infractions have recently resulted in the temporary closing of some fraternity houses.

Financial Aid

Applicants with a 3.2 high school GPA may be awarded merit scholarships, but these are only semester by semester to ensure persistent academic performance. Just attending a **Visit Weekend** can result in a $1000 award and **Linfield First** scholarships support many **First Generation** students. Music scholarships are also generous.

Study Away

Linfield encourages its students to adventure abroad, and 8-12 exciting faculty-led courses are offered each January term to destinations both within the U.S. and in regions across the globe. Because Linfield believes global experience is very beneficial, the university pays round trip airfare for your first study trip abroad.

Evenstad Center for Wine Education

Linfield University's Evenstad Center for Wine Education integrates numerous wine education programs and activities into academic and experiential learning for undergraduates and adult learners. It is committed to building connections between growers, wineries, businesses, and students throughout the wine industry.

The goals of the Evenstad Center are to provide a unique, interdisciplinary liberal arts study of all aspects of wine, prepare potential future leaders of the wine industry, create opportunities for faculty research and development, and preserve and document the history of the Oregon Wine Industry.

Similar programs and institutes in wine science and management studies are offered at Washington State U, Central Washington U, Walla Walla Community College, and the University of British Columbia-Okanagan.

Linfield University Basic Statistics

Undergraduate Enrollment	Freshman Class Enrollment	Institution Total Enrollment	Female/Male Student Ratio	Female/Male Faculty Ratio	Student/ Faculty Ratio
1762	315	1798	67/33	57/43	10/1
# of 1st Year Applications	**# of 1st Year Women Admitted**	**# of 1st Year Men Admitted**	**# of Transfer Students Admitted**	**Overall Yield**	**% of Out-of-State Students**
2229	1182	675	188	17%	33%
% Students Living in Campus Housing	**Fraternity/ Sorority Participation**	**% Students Receiving Need-based Aid**	**1st Year Students Retention Rate**	**% Classes Under 30**	**% Caucasian/ White Faculty**
55%	23% / 17%	77%	81.1%	90%	83%
# Caucasian / White Students	**# Hispanic / Latinx Students**	**# Asian Students**	**# Black Students**	**# American Indian/ Alaskan, Hawaiian /Native Pacific Islander**	**# International Students**
1129	310	103	26	16	18
In-State Tuition and Fees	**Room and Board**	**Out-of-State Tuition and Fees**	**Honors Program Cost**	**Honors Program Grant**	**Athletic Division**
$47,350	$13,600	$47,350	n/a	n/a	NCAA Div.III

Notes:

Pacific Lutheran University

Tacoma, Washington / www. plu.edu

PLU has a strong global perspective, a focus on inclusion, and a mission to help students discover a vocational calling that includes meaningful service to others and joyful fulfillment in their lives and careers.

Location

The port city of Tacoma, with a population of about 200,000, is situated on beautiful Puget Sound in western Washington, with easy access to SEA-TAC International Airport and Seattle. The temperate climate and a great waterfront, a 700 acre park, public beaches, and the nearby Cascades mountain range, plus relatively affordable living, have combined over the years to attract artists and musicians who have produced thriving cultural resources within the city.

The expansive Pacific Lutheran University campus is located south of city center, but there is good bus transportation into the downtown's renowned theater district. This area offers multiple venues for live performances, and a wide variety of stores, galleries, restaurants, and pubs.

Community

Although a Lutheran-affiliated institution, PLU focuses not on a specific faith but on being called, with others, to a vocation that promotes human and ecological flourishing. This commitment is at the heart of the University's welcoming, collaborative, inclusive, and supportive community spirit. PLU is intentionally diverse. Over 40% of its 2900 undergrads identify as other than white/non-Hispanic, and 42% of first year students are First Generation.

A majority of PLU students come from Washington State. The 156 acre wooded campus makes for a peacefully beautiful enclave sometimes referred to as a "bubble." However, there are ample opportunities for PLU's students to be a force for change in whatever direction they choose, and student voices are heard and valued in class discussions and through active student clubs.

The community is serious about promoting inclusivity and a sense of belonging for every student. It develops programs and events that challenge students to ask hard questions about controversial issues that impact their community and view them from a global perspective. Student clubs and organizations provide an active social life, community engagement, service, and fun events. Multiple options for being involved in music and theater groups provide avenues for creative self–expression.

Academics

PLU's strong Business and Health Professions departments attract about twenty percent of students as majors, followed closely by the social sciences, physical sciences, and visual and performing arts. Students seem to agree that professors are communicative, supportive, accommodating, and teach passionately.

Ample resources are put toward academic support for students through the **Center for Student Success.** The **First Year Experience** program is interdisciplinary and encourages critical thinking from multiple perspectives. It also features off-campus expeditions and experiential learning. In addition, all new students engage in the Common Reading Program, in which they read the same book and share their responses as a community.

The competitive **International Honors Program** provides an alternative to the General Education curriculum and requires a service and academic achievement record for acceptance. An innovative Business and Economic History program has a generous endowment that also provides a funded fellowship for summer research.

The **PLU School of Arts and Communication** describes its mission as "developing processes for sustainable cultural enhancement" and includes a minor in the Publishing and Printing arts. The Communications program has an award-winning student-run **Media Lab,** home to a Documentary Studies program that produces acclaimed investigative documentaries. Students manage a student newspaper, radio station, and TV channel, giving them valuable experience for future careers in the field. The music and theater programs are holistic in approach and present hundreds of events and performances each year.

Student-faculty research is well established and well-funded. Opportunities for internships include a **Natural Science Summer Undergraduate Research Program.** Nordic Studies is an option as well. The popular Psychology program encourages and celebrates student research at a Research Conference. A 4-1-4 academic calendar allows for a one month January term and two four-week Summer Terms. A class in Transitions and Trauma recently traveled to Prague during a January Term study period.

Student Activities and Residential Life

The 80 clubs and organizations available to students at PLU provide something for everyone except Greek life. Twelve choral and instrumental ensembles, plus dance, theater, speech and debate, newspaper, television, and a literary magazine, give students even more avenues for creative self-expression.

Everyone who lives on campus becomes part of a **Learning Community (LC)** either by year or by theme (*STEM or Creative Expression, etc.*), and first year students enroll in linked courses related to their LC. Students report that the food is good and special preferences are accommodated. Two cafes and a market, as well as the main dining hall, are all owned by the University, not contracted out. There are eight residence halls, and the roommate matching process for first year students is caring and attentive to inclusion and individual needs.

Varsity Athletes compete in the Northwest Conference in nine men's sports and ten women's Division III sports, including the nationally-ranked women's rowing team. Club teams, Intramurals. and Outdoor Recreation are available for all skill levels. PLU has a competition pool, the **Names Fitness Center,** the **Memorial Gym,** and ample outdoor playing fields, courts, and track.

Financial Aid

Merit scholarships include the President's and the Harstad Founders scholarships and many more based on merit and community service records. 98% of students receive some level of financial aid.

Study Away

There is also aid available from a $2 million **Gates Study Away** fund that increases opportunities for low income students. The **English and Global Studies** program takes a group of students to the U.K. to study during J-Term. Other departments have similar innovative study trips. PLU's **Wang Center for Global and Community Engaged Education** provides guidance in choosing among the many options available. 50% of PLU students choose a study away option at some point.

Living Learning Communities

Living/Learning Communities (LLCs) within on-campus housing have gained popularity at many colleges and universities. The primary goals are to increase academic and community engagement and help students build a network of friends with whom they share interests.

These LLCs can be located on a floor or wing of a dorm or involve an entire residential hall. The organizing factor can be an academic interest such as engineering, a passion for outdoor recreation, be centered on identity or cultural heritage, or be a shared commitment to sustainable living.

The options are unlimited and will vary from one college to another. Working together, the LLC advisors, faculty mentors, and students develop programs that enhance academics and broaden social horizons. These teams introduce new students to campus resources such as mental health and tutoring services, design service projects, have dinner discussions, and invite speakers to community get-togethers.

At their best, such LLCs can and do make a big difference in first year students' transition to college and provide them with the essential resources, information, and contacts they need to make their college experience fun and productive.

Pacific Lutheran University Basic Statistics

Undergraduate Enrollment	Freshman Class Enrollment	Institution Total Enrollment	Female/Male Student Ratio	Female/Male Faculty Ratio	Student/ Faculty Ratio
2,373	510	2,706	65/35	57/43	13/1
# of 1st Year Applications	**# of 1st Year Women Admitted**	**# of 1st Year Men Admitted**	**# of Transfer Students Admitted**	**Overall Yield**	**% of Out-of-State Students**
3,220	1,744	1,101	449	18%	22%
% Students Living in Campus Housing	**Fraternity/ Sorority Participation**	**% Students Receiving Need-based Aid**	**1st Year Students Retention Rate**	**% Classes Under 30**	**% Caucasian/ White Faculty**
48%	0	74%	78.53%	82%	82%
# Caucasian / White Students	**# Hispanic / Latinx Students**	**# Asian Students**	**# Black Students**	**# American Indian/ Alaskan, Hawaiian /Native Pacific Islander**	**# International Students**
1,275	374	262	82	48	27
In-State Tuition and Fees	**Room and Board**	**Out-of-State Tuition and Fees**	**Honors Program Cost**	**Honors Program Grant**	**Athletic Division**
$50,928	$11,826	$50,928	n/a	n/a	NCAA Div.III

Notes:

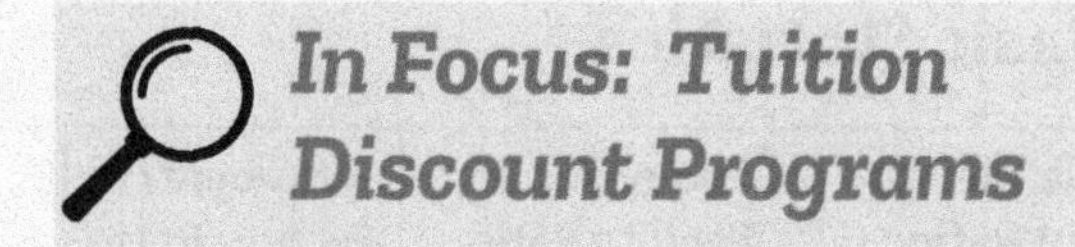

In Focus: Tuition Discount Programs

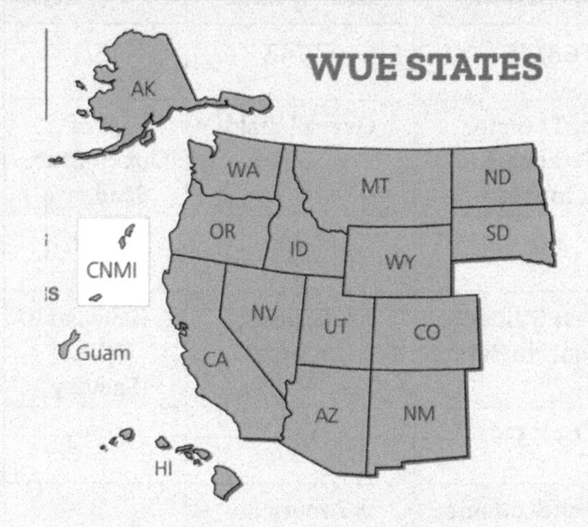

The **Western University Exchange (WUE)** fosters agreements among public colleges and universities across 15 member states and territories to make their campuses affordable to out of state (*non-residential*) students through a **WUE scholarship**. Eligible students pay no more than 150% of the in-state tuition rate.

Some institutions limit WUE exchange scholarships to students with a certain minimum GPA, some exclude certain majors, and some limit the total number of incoming students they offer the savings program to each year. Application deadlines for WUE discounts can vary, so it is best to apply as early as possible.

To be eligible for a WUE savings program, the student must be a resident of one of the following participating states or territories and be applying to a public college or university located in a different state or territory. **Alaska, Arizona, California, Colorado, Commonwealth of the Northern Mariana Islands (CNMI), Federated States of Micronesia (FSM), Guam, Hawai'i, Idaho, Montana, Nevada, New Mexico, North Dakota, Oregon, Republic of the Marshall Islands (RMI), South Dakota, Utah, Washington, or Wyoming**.

Other reciprocity agreements and exchanges at PNW colleges and universities:

California students from certain high schools may receive Oregon resident tuition at **Southern Oregon University.**

Portland State U has a **Washington Border Policy** limited to Washington state residents who live in 11 approved border counties to attend Portland State University part-time and be assessed resident tuition rates.

Some **Washington State community colleges** and branch campuses also have limited tuition waiver programs for students from border counties.

Non-Resident Tuition Waivers (NRTWs) are used as a recruitment tool for top students at several public community colleges and universities. Most are essentially very competitive merit scholarships. Incoming international undergraduates may also be able to benefit from an NRTW.

The University of Idaho offers an **Invitation to Idaho Scholarship** for out of state students who are not residents of a WUE state and have at least a 3.0 GPA.

Boise State University offers **Incoming Nonresident Scholarships** with some limitations.

Montana State University provides **Achievement** and **Blue and Gold Scholarships** to students from out of state, but these are not stackable with WUE scholarships.

Private College Special Scholarships for Out of State students:

Carroll College offers **Advantage Awards** of $2000-$10,000 to Montana, Idaho, and Oregon students with financial need and **INSPIRE** scholarships to Everett, WA. public high school graduates and a Catholic High School Room Grant for graduates of a Catholic high school.

Lewis and Clark College offers scholarships up to $5000 for students from Lemhi or Custer County high schools in Idaho.

Members of American Indian Tribes applying to PNW public universities may receive tuition waivers.

A student who is not a resident of Washington but who is a member of a federally recognized American Indian tribe and who has lived for a year in one—or a combination of several—designated states (*Idaho, Montana, Oregon, or Washington*), is considered a resident of Washington for tuition purposes.

The Oregon Tribal Student Grant program was established for 2022-23 to provide grants to eligible Oregon tribal students to offset the cost of attendance for attending eligible Oregon colleges and universities. Enrolled members of a federally recognized tribe of Oregon or of a tribe that had traditional and customary boundaries in parts of the state or that cede or reserved lands within the State of Oregon will be considered a resident for tuition purposes. Montana has a similar program.

University of Portland

Portland, Oregon / www. up.edu

This prominent Catholic university offers an intimate city-based campus, solid preparation for life and professional careers, and a welcoming community focused on the holistic education of heart and mind and global responsibility for others.

Location

Portland, population 645,000, is one of the greenest cities in the U.S., not only in the amount of open space devoted to its 279 parks, but also in its environmental consciousness and social activism. Located close to both the Pacific Ocean coast and the rugged Cascade Mountains range, it is highly walkable and noted for unique neighborhoods that are fun to explore, including a thriving twelve block **Culture District**.

Aerial tram commuting, Portland , OR

Portland's International airport (PDX) and the expansive city transportation system are both outstanding. Like many cities, there is a noticeable homeless problem. Workplaces are casual and laid back and most people cope well with Portland's weather, which in Jan-March can be grey and rainy, in contrast to the quite nice weather in other seasons.

Community

As a Catholic University UP's mission focuses on holistic development of self, ethical reflection, faith, and reason, and on preparing students for service to the needs of others. The intimate UP campus, with its verdant tree-lined lawns, sits on a high bluff overlooking the Willamette River and the city.

Holy Cross brothers and priests live and minister in UP's residential halls, assisting the staff in providing supportive living and learning environments that foster a holistic education of the heart and mind.

UP is well-diversified, with 49% of students identifying as other than White and 72% of students coming from out of state. About 30% percent of students identify as Catholic.

The community is a welcoming one that offers solid preparation for a meaningful life and successful career. This is not a party school but rather a welcoming and warm environment in which most students are serious about working toward a fulfilling career and the faculty members and staff are supportive and open.

Academics

Nursing, Engineering, and Business are by far the most popular majors. The curriculum is challenging but manageable if you put in the effort, according to students. Most students in these popular majors come to UP having already decided on which field of study they want to pursue.

Class sizes are generally under thirty students, and professors get good reviews from students on quality of teaching and level of care about their individual success. Students report that the professors are accessible and encourage them to come to their offices for help.

The **Shepard Academic Resources Center** provides special programs for first generation students and comprehensive services for all students needing learning assistance or accommodations. The **STEM Education and Outreach Center** not only supports multiple science and engineering clubs and Honors Societies but also works with the North Portland public schools to help improve the quality of K-12 STEM education.

University of Portland's Nursing Program is considered outstanding, and admission to it is very competitive. UP's **Dundon-Berchthol Institute** supports and encourages student-faculty research and internships focusing on the importance of understanding how personal values influence moral character and our ethical life and work decisions. The **Franz Center for Leadership, Entrepreneurship and Innovation** offers an Entrepreneurial Scholars Program, a Pilot Venture Challenge, and a Lecture Series to encourage students in innovative business and creative community leadership.

Students grumble about the three required Core courses in **Religion, Faith and Ethics**, but accept them as a given in an institution with a deep commitment not only to the education of heart and mind but also to global responsibility for the common good. The UP **Honors Program** mentors high achieving students, encourages their research and creative activities and works with them on applying to post graduate fellowships. All students are encouraged to do internships and Portland city offers a wide range of internship options.

Recreational Activities and Residential Life

All first year students must live on campus. UP offers three coed, three female-only, and three male-only residence halls plus coed apartments of different sizes for upper class and graduate students. Each hall has professional staff plus a Holy Cross pastoral resident. UP is not a party school, but each residence hall has a quirky individual personality and hosts events and programs that enrich the University's calendar of social gatherings and fun events. Designated quiet hours are observed in all residences. Students are enthusiastic about the food service.

Special interest clubs and organizations such as Gender and Sexuality, ethnic community clubs such as the Latinix Student Union, The Moreau Center for Service and Justice, Cheerleading Squad, Writer's Magazine, and KDUP radio are active on campus.

The **Recreation and Wellness Center** has workout space, fitness studios, playing courts, and a climbing wall and supports intramural leagues and Sports Clubs and an Outdoor Recreation program. Six men's and eight women's teams compete at the Division I level. Weekends are quiet on the UP campus, but Portland city invites exploration and engagement.

Financial Aid

UP offers numerous merit aid scholarships and also institutional grants for lower income students, depending on level of need. About 97% of first year students receive some level of financial aid. Air Force and Army ROTC programs offer special assistance for those interested in military service.

Study Away

Nursing students can enjoy a semester program at the **University of Notre Dame, Australia,** and get core credits and one nursing course, and other students can choose from various credit courses.

UP has its own **Salzburg Center** in Austria with housing and study, including German language study. UP students can join Willamette University students in a spring semester at the **National University of Ireland,** Galway. Business students can take a semester at **Kookmin University** in Korea, where classes are taught in English.

Study Centers Abroad

Developing global citizens with intercultural competencies for today's global economy is imperative. Most institutions have a large selection of approved study away programs offered in countries around the world, usually through various agencies and organizations such as the **American Institute for Foreign Study** (AIFS). Most also have a study abroad office on campus with staff who advise students and assist them in planning.

Some colleges and universities have collaborative arrangements or partnerships with a specific international academic center that offers a program or programs that are good fits for their students in specific majors.

The **UP Salzburg Center** in Austria is one of the few centers that are actually owned or rented by the home university. This means UP designs the curricular options and has local faculty and a program director on the Center's staff. Gonzaga University has a similar **Gonzaga in Florence** campus (GIF) in Florence, Italy, which is extremely popular with its students.

University of Portland Basic Statistics

Undergraduate Enrollment	Freshman Class Enrollment	Institution Total Enrollment	Female/Male Student Ratio	Female/Male Faculty Ratio	Student/ Faculty Ratio
3,587	911	4,029	62/38	53/47	11/1
# of 1st Year Applications	**# of 1st Year Women Admitted**	**# of 1st Year Men Admitted**	**# of Transfer Students Admitted**	**Overall Yield**	**% of Out-of-State Students**
12,044	6,657	3,121	165	9.3%	71.7%
% Students Living in Campus Housing	**Fraternity/ Sorority Participation**	**% Students Receiving Need-based Aid**	**1st Year Students Retention Rate**	**% Classes Under 30**	**% Caucasian/ White Faculty**
50%	n/a	59%	90%	89%	84%
# Caucasian / White Students	**# Hispanic / Latinx Students**	**# Asian Students**	**# Black Students**	**# American Indian/ Alaskan, Hawaiian /Native Pacific Islander**	**# International Students**
1,738	530	696	72	55	96
In-State Tuition and Fees	**Room and Board**	**Out-of-State Tuition and Fees**	**Honors Program Cost**	**Honors Program Grant**	**Athletic Division**
$49,494	$15,356	$49,494	n/a	n/a	NCAA Div.I

Notes:

University of Puget Sound

Tacoma, Washington / www.pugetsound.edu

UPS offers a rigorous liberal arts education focused on civic and community engagement, professional career programs, a conservatory of music, and innovative residential housing in a lively city setting.

Location

The port city of Tacoma, population 200,000 is situated on beautiful Puget Sound in western Washington, with easy access to SEA-TAC International Airport and Seattle. Bus and ferry services provide long distance transportation as does Amtrak, which goes north to Vancouver, B.C. and south to Portland.

Puget Sound, WA

The temperate climate and a great waterfront, a 700 acre park, public beaches, and the nearby Cascades mountain range, plus relatively affordable living, have combined over the years to attract artists and musicians who have produced thriving cultural resources within the city.

Students from the three private and two public universities in the vicinity find Tacoma offers dining, recreation, and exploration options. A city bus stop is just 5 mins from the UPS campus for easy access to the downtown area.

Community

UPS students mention the strong sense of community at UPS as an attraction along with its beautiful campus. Almost three-quarters of the 2200 students at UPS are from out of state. The University is noted for being LBGTQ inclusive and students speak of developing a sense of belonging during their first year experience.

UPS strongly encourages student leadership. It has been recognized as producing the highest undergraduate voting rate among the eight hundred and forty institutions that participated in the 2020 Campus Democracy Challenge. The **Office of Intercultural Engagement** and the **Civic Engagement and Leadership Program** focus on civic and global engagement and responsibility.

Students are also active in community service. The **Race and Pedagogy Institute** at UPS brings attention to critical social issues for both the campus and Tacoma communities.

Academics

Student reviews mention the high level of engagement and warm support that students receive from faculty members and refer to this as the University's strongest asset.

Intimate class sizes are typical at UPS and classes are described as thought-provoking and rigorous. The **Sound Policy Institute** is a hub for the community's efforts to incorporate experiential learning and sustainability issues discussion into courses through field trips, events, and internships. The UPS **School of Music** and **School of Business and Leadership** attract students looking for pre-professional programs.

Seminars in Argument and Inquiry serve as the foundation for Core courses across the five major academic fields. Interdisciplinary **Connections Courses** have interesting titles, such as The Economics of Happiness and The Idea of Wine. However, some Connections courses are only offered intermittingly. Students must also satisfy a **Knowledge, Identity, and Power** requirement by taking a course examining the dynamics of power, inequality, and division in societies.

The University's popular Asian Languages and Culture program offers Chinese, Japanese, and basic Arabic, and some students pursue this as a dual degree with International Business.

UPS also offers a Healthcare Administration and Leadership program, and a substantial number of options in the School of Engineering and Computer Science. An innovative 'blended pathway' allows students to complete a Master's degree in one of the engineering fields in just five years. UPS has a well-regarded Conservatory of Music offering five majors, including Music Industry Studies, Music Management, and Music Therapy.

The **Coolidge Otis Chapman Honors Program** includes residential opportunities and special programs, as well as challenging seminars that cover the core requirements through intriguing courses such as Mathematics of Symmetry and Metamorphosis and Identity, and culminates in a Senior Thesis. UPS has a **Phi Beta Kappa** chapter.

Recreational Activities and Residential Life

All first year students live in traditional campus dorms. Older students have a choice of suite style living or a room in one of fifty University-owned homes in the adjacent residential neighborhood. These houses accommodate small groups of sophomores, juniors, and seniors who want to live with others who share their interests. Trans and non-binary students' individual needs are respected and accommodated. Some residence halls also have themes such as Outdoor Exploration. Competition for places in the residential houses can be challenging. UPS **Honors Program** students can choose a residence hall or one of the neighborhood houses. Greek life is well established on this campus with eight chapter houses, four fraternities, and five sororities.

Multiple clubs and organizations provide ample opportunities to get involved in everything from student-published magazines to music and arts groups to religious and identity-based groups. The list of more than forty student organizations begins with an African Alliance Club and ends with WIXEN *(Women's Intersectionality, Empowerment and Narratives)* and includes many and varied culturally based, issue based, and faith based clubs.

The **Names Fitness Center,** the **Memorial Gym**, the **Olson Fieldhouse,** the PLU pool and several sports fields inspire students to participate in fitness training and Intramural sports. Club Sports fill niches for those wanting to keep active in a favorite sport or explore a new competitive sport. Lacrosse, Wrestling, and Crew are among the most popular Club Sports. PLU Varsity athletes compete in thirteen sports, including swimming, in NCAA Division III in the Northwest Conference.

Financial Aid

Merit scholarships are offered and high achieving students can compete for the prestigious **Lillis** and **Matelich Scholarships,** each of which covers most expenses. The college also works with the POSSE Scholars program in supporting diverse and low income students.

Study Away

The UPS **Wang Center** offers a variety of study abroad programs. Some programs are faculty-led, and some are collaborative department programs. These include the **Kyoto Summer** program and the **Oaxaca; Development, Cultural and Social Change** program at **Instituto Cultural Oaxaca.**

Phi Beta Kappa

Phi Beta Kappa is our nation's most prestigious academic honor society for liberal arts and sciences students. Only ten percent of U.S. colleges and universities (290) have Phi Beta Kappa chapters, and these chapters invite only the top students at their institutions to become members.

Such members must be juniors or seniors majoring in and excelling in a traditional liberal arts or sciences degree program, have knowledge of a second language, and be of good moral character. Once inducted into Phi Beta Kappa, the student is able to enjoy lifelong membership.

To be awarded a Phi Beta Chapter, the higher education institution must undergo an extensive evaluation. New chapters are added only every three years.

University of Puget Sound Basic Statistics

Undergraduate Enrollment	Freshman Class Enrollment	Institution Total Enrollment	Female/Male Student Ratio	Female/Male Faculty Ratio	Student/ Faculty Ratio
1,866	409	2,173	60/40	57/43	10/1
# of 1st Year Applications	**# of 1st Year Women Admitted**	**# of 1st Year Men Admitted**	**# of Transfer Students Admitted**	**Overall Yield**	**% of Out-of-State Students**
5,025	2,406	2,031	98	9%	71%
% Students Living in Campus Housing	**Fraternity/ Sorority Participation**	**% Students Receiving Need-based Aid**	**1st Year Students Retention Rate**	**% Classes Under 30**	**% Caucasian/ White Faculty**
66%	25% / 24%	54%	88%	96%	84%
# Caucasian / White Students	**# Hispanic / Latinx Students**	**# Asian Students**	**# Black Students**	**# American Indian/ Alaskan, Hawaiian /Native Pacific Islander**	**# International Students**
1,211	224	142	48	15	5
In-State Tuition and Fees	**Room and Board**	**Out-of-State Tuition and Fees**	**Honors Program Cost**	**Honors Program Grant**	**Athletic Division**
$57,206	$13,430	$57,206	0	varies	NCAA III

Notes:

Quest University

Squamish, British Columbia / www.quest.ca

Intellectually adventurous students, and students whose individual competitive sport or entertainment career requires a flexible academic calendar, find Quest University and its stunningly beautiful natural environment a perfect match.

Location

Just an hour north of the city of Vancouver, Squamish is a deep water port town located on Howe Sound. The rugged Garibaldi Mountains on one side have granite cliffs reaching to 9400 ft. above the town. The community of 23,000 is one of the fastest growing in Canada, and cost of living is relatively high. The Sea to Sky Highway 99 links residents to metro Vancouver and to world famous Whistler Ski resort which is just thirty minutes to the north.

Whistler Ski Resort, British Columbia

The climate is surprisingly mild, with comfortable summers but cold and snowy winters. Each light-filled, LEED Certified, 21st -century modern building on Quest's 90 acre hilltop campus frames a stunning view of the natural landscapes that surround the University.

Community

Quest's intimate and eclectic community represents as many as forty different countries. The community consists of students and faculty who share similar concepts regarding what constitutes excellence in higher education learning but their individual interests and career goals may differ widely. Student engagement is exceptional here and collaboration is a key element in both academics and extracurricular activities. The decision to attend Quest requires deliberate self-reflection as to personal learning style and self-motivation.

Quest's **LEAP Program** accommodates students who are highly competitive Individual Athletics competitors or who have demanding Performance Careers and need flexibility in their academic schedules.

The **Quest Student Association** takes the lead role in developing community programs, initiatives, events, and clubs and offers opportunities for leadership and fostering of creative ideas. A peer-organized **Gender, Sex and Sexuality Resource Center** and a **Wellness Program** address student needs. The student community often includes elite individual sports athletes or film, stage, or music performers, because they can leverage their athletic training and competition, or their performance and recording schedules, with Quest's Block Plan and academic calendar. This private university recently restructured due to financial problems, but has survived and benefitted from the process.

Academics

With Quest's **Block** academic calendar, students take only one course at a time for an intensive 3.5 week period. This allows for deep immersion in the course topic. Seminar classes ensure close engagement and collaboration among students and faculty members. Foundational studies include life and physical sciences, math, social science, art and humanities, and language combined with activities that build the student's critical thinking and compelling argument skills. The **Learning Commons** provides inviting spaces where students work together and with **Peer Tutors** to address questions about, or challenges with the course materials. Committed to teaching, Quest faculty are also outstanding researchers in their fields.

Quest offers one degree; a Bachelor of Arts and Sciences. Students spend their final two years developing and completing a **Keystone Project,** which addresses a unique **Key Question** that the student has chosen to research in-depth and in-breadth. With ample support from a faculty mentor, the student builds their degree, shaping and defining it in ways that are customized to their own creative, intellectual, and societal interests. During this **Concentration Period,** students select a variety of focus, experiential, and elective courses which explore, inform, and help define the parameters of their Keystone Project research. A **Summer Fellows Program** also offers faculty-student collaborative research opportunities.

Recreational Activities and Residential Life

Most Quest students live on campus in one of three residence halls through their third year. All students have a private bedroom with sink while sharing a bathroom with one other neighbor. Students are required to have a meal plan, and the food is delicious, healthy, and fresh, and all dietary needs are honored.

Students can get involved with the student newspaper, Model UN, an academic journal, a poet's society, a beekeeping club, a bouldering gym, xcountry skiing, and an Improv group, among other options.

The geothermally heated RecPlex offers space for intramural sports, fitness studios, and bouldering gym, with adjacent all-weather soccer field and tennis courts. The area's outdoor recreation opportunities are vast. Hiking and biking, kiteboarding and kayaking, white water rafting, rock climbing, and bouldering are all easily accessed. Whistler Ski Resort and Olympic Park are just up the road.

Instead of varsity team sports, the LEAP program assists and supports elite athletes who excel in individual sports, and many of these LEAP scholar-athletes compete at National, Olympic, and Paralympic levels.

Financial Aid

Quest offers achievement and potential-based scholarships and financial need grants to students. Quest students with U.S. citizenship have access to U.S. Federal Student Aid (FSA) loans, but not Pell grants.

Scholarships are available for high achieving Canadian and Global Citizens, and for Leaders in Elite Athletics and Performance (LEAP), as well as a **Presidential Scholarship** based on GPA, and a **Quest Spirit Award** for a student who embodies the spirit of Quest.

Study Away

70% of Quest students spend one or two academic periods abroad at Quest's wide range of Study Abroad partner institutions. These include three US private colleges, including Colorado College, as well as universities in other countries.

Students can also do a shorter **Language Immersion** at any accredited university where the language studied is that of the local community. Field research courses, such as Quest's **Antarctica Field Course**, also involve expeditions abroad.

Block Study Plans

The traditional college schedule offers courses in two semester, or three term segments between September and May. Students take a number of courses concurrently during each segment. Some institutions also offer some shorter courses within those semesters or terms. This means that these college students are taking several courses concurrently, just as they did in high school, and must balance their time in order to handle their course load efficiently. With traditional term and semester calendars, any extended study and fieldwork trips can only be scheduled for vacation periods, during January terms, or during summer break.

A Block Plan offers another option. In a Block Plan students take a series of short intense blocks of study on one topic or subject, with a break between each block, or at least take one block per semester of intense study on one subject.

Students who enjoy concentrating on one subject or topic at a time, and benefit from intense, but time limited, engagement, are attracted by the idea of a block plan college schedule. One advantage of the block schedule is that it allows time for a class to travel and study off campus during any block period. The Block plan also enables students to plan short study exchanges between colleges with similar block schedules, such as between Quest University and Colorado College.

Among our Pacific University institutions, Quest University and Montana Western University offer full-year block plans, while Alaska Pacific University offers a modified block schedule each semester.

Quest University Basic Statistics

Undergraduate Enrollment	Freshman Class Enrollment	Institution Total Enrollment	Female/Male Student Ratio	Female/Male Faculty Ratio	Student/ Faculty Ratio
--	--	420	49/51	--	5/1
# of 1st Year Applications	**# of 1st Year Women Admitted**	**# of 1st Year Men Admitted**	**# of Transfer Students Admitted**	**Overall Yield**	**% of Out-of-State Students**
--	--	--	--	--	45%
% Students Living in Campus Housing	**Fraternity/ Sorority Participation**	**% Students Receiving Need-based Aid**	**1st Year Students Retention Rate**	**% Classes Under 30**	**% Caucasian/ White Faculty**
100%	0	85%	--	100%	--
# Caucasian / White Students	**# Hispanic / Latinx Students**	**# Asian Students**	**# Black Students**	**# American Indian/ Alaskan, Hawaiian /Native Pacific Islander**	**# International Students**
--	--	--	--	--	45%
In-Canada Tuition and Fees	**Room and Board**	**Out-of-Canada Tuition and Fees**	**Honors Program Cost**	**Honors Program Grant**	**Athletic Division**
$21,219 CAD*	$14,300 CAD*	$35,219 CAD*	n/a	n/a	n/a

* Canadian dollars

Notes:

Reed College

Portland, Oregon / www.reed.edu

This unique small college attracts highly motivated and deeply curious student scholars who enjoy debate, argumentation, creative exploration, and experimentation within an intellectually stimulating and academically challenging environment.

Location

Portland, population 645,000, is situated at the confluence of the Columbia and Willamette Rivers. Noted for its environmental consciousness and social activism, it is also one of the greenest cities in the US, with open space devoted to 279 parks. Located fairly close to both the Pacific Ocean coast and the rugged Cascade Mountains range, the city is highly walkable and has unique neighborhoods that are fun to explore, including a thriving twelve block **Culture District** filled with art galleries, bookstores, and performance venues. Like many U.S. cities, Portland has a noticeable homeless problem.

Lan Su Chinese Garden, Portland Oregon

Work places are casual and laid back and most residents cope well with Portland's weather, which in Jan-March can be grey and rainy, in contrast to the quite nice weather in other seasons. The International airport and the expansive city transportation system are both outstanding.

Community

Reed's handsome 116 acre campus is situated in a quiet, upscale Southeast Portland community. The college is known for its intellectual intensity and for producing graduates who go on to Ph.D. programs in both STEM and liberal arts fields, and to law and medical schools.

Reed's sense of community is founded on active student and faculty scholarly engagement that confronts intellectual challenges with grit and humor. Students adhere to an **Honor Principle** and are very protective of their rights to participate in academic policies and planning decisions. They hold faculty, students, and administrators accountable. Reed attracts 90% of its students from states other than Oregon, and International students make up about 9% of the student population.

Reed's somewhat insular culture, often referred to as a "bubble," is one in which students look out for one another and collaborate in solving community issues and conflicts in ways that promote peaceful coexistence. Volunteerism and community service are strongly encouraged. **SEEDS** (*Students for Education, Equity, and Direct Service*) offers many opportunities for volunteers and also provides off campus options for earning Work Study wages for work at community organizations and **Community Education** credits toward fulfilling a graduation requirement.

Academics

At Reed, all first year students take a rigorous one-year humanities course focusing on writing, active preparation, constructive conference participation, and argumentation skills. Distribution requirements include humanities and art courses, history and social science, and natural, mathematical, and psychological sciences.

Reed professors are noted for superb teaching, demanding coursework, and classes that focus on collaborative learning. Rather than grades, students receive oral and written evaluations, and as a result, students are less competitive with each other. Student comments about the administrative side of the college are less positive.

By the end of sophomore year, students declare a major, submit an individually designed plan for completing all requirements for that major, and then take relevant courses in their junior year. Near the end of junior year, students must pass a qualifying exam before beginning their senior year thesis. This is an opportunity to gauge what support or additional work the student may need to complete before launching into their thesis research and development.

In their senior year students complete any remaining course requirements and focus on their chosen thesis problem. This problem can be a creative, experimental, or critical one. The thesis is developed with support from a faculty thesis advisor. Prior to graduation, the student takes a final oral exam. Theses and majors are frequently interdisciplinary, and double majors are possible. Independent study is limited to just one course in the junior or senior year. Funded summer research opportunities with Reed faculty or faculty from another institution are available to ambitious students.

Recreational Activities and Residential Life

The **Reed Outdoor Education Center** offers programs focused on physical well-being through outdoor adventures and with expeditions in and around the Portland area. The college supports several coached and regionally competitive **Club Sports,** but the College does not have a varsity athletic program. The campus **Sports Center** has a pool, climbing wall, racquetball, handball, squash courts, workout equipment, fitness studio spaces, and adjacent sports fields.

The first year student residential neighborhood has eight residence halls where programs support a smooth transition to college. Eleven sophomore residences offer communal environments with kitchens for small numbers of students and single rooms, and there are several language houses. Juniors and seniors have options for college-owned apartment living right on campus, or can reside off-campus, which is the choice of about 50% of students after sophomore year. In the college's attractive **Commons** building, the food service serves healthy, vegetarian friendly food.

Financial Aid

Reed College meets one hundred percent of full demonstrated need using a combination of institutional funds and Federal student loans and grants. All financial aid is based on need. There are no merit grants or merit based scholarships. Over fifty-five percent of Reed students receive need based financial aid.

Study Away

Reed partners with many other top liberal arts colleges and three domestic institutions to offer a wide variety of **Exchange Programs.** These do require careful preliminary planning to fit into a student's rigorous eight-semester academic plan.

Reed also offers internships and fellowships with international study options. Students receiving financial aid may apply their aid to the cost of their Reed international program

Club Sports

Collegiate Club Sports are increasingly popular with college students who have loved playing and competing in a team sport in high school but who do not want to prioritize it over their academic studies and career preparation.

Club Sports are a step up from the intramural games most colleges and universities offer through their recreation departments. Club Sports are organized, are competitive in that they play against other colleges and often in leagues, may or may not have a paid coach and some level of sponsorship from the college or university, and will usually be managed by the students themselves.

Club sports can offer a student a new and challenging opportunity to learn and play another sport; anyone for Quidditch? Rodeo? Kayaking?

Club sports are not registered with **NCAA** or **NAIA**. Still, many have governing bodies such as the **United States College Ski Association** or the **National Scholastic Surfing Association,** or **USA Ultimate**, who set rules and regulations for play. USA Ultimate's mission, for instance, is *"to advance the sport of Ultimate in the United States by enhancing and promoting Character, Community, and Competition."*

Reed College Basic Statistics

Undergraduate Enrollment	Freshman Class Enrollment	Institution Total Enrollment	Female/Male Student Ratio	Female/Male Faculty Ratio	Student/ Faculty Ratio
1,548	502	1,566	58/42	46/54	9/1
# of 1st Year Applications	**# of 1st Year Women Admitted**	**# of 1st Year Men Admitted**	**# of Transfer Students Admitted**	**Overall Yield**	**% of Out-of-State Students**
7,010	1874	999	41	16%	90%
% Students Living in Campus Housing	**Fraternity/ Sorority Participation**	**% Students Receiving Need-based Aid**	**1st Year Students Retention Rate**	**% Classes Under 30**	**% Caucasian/ White Faculty**
70%	0	57%	87.36%	97%	78%
# Caucasian / White Students	**# Hispanic / Latinx Students**	**# Asian Students**	**# Black Students**	**# American Indian/ Alaskan, Hawaiian /Native Pacific Islander**	**# International Students**
910	171	124	20	2	137
In-State Tuition and Fees	**Room and Board**	**Out-of-State Tuition and Fees**	**Honors Program Cost**	**Honors Program Grant**	**Athletic Division**
$64,760	$15,950	$64,760	n/a	n/a	n/a

Notes:

In Focus: LGBTQIA+ Inclusion and Support

Colleges and universities in the Cascadia bioregion welcome LGBTQIA+ applicants, but some are ahead of others in creating the programs and services that build an inclusive campus culture and ensure that students of all identities have the resources needed to thrive.

The nonprofit organization **Campus Pride** offers U.S. Higher Ed institutions assistance as they work toward understanding and responding to LBGTQIA+ students' needs. Not all institutions are included in the Campus Pride Index Ranking System because an institution must apply for this assistance and some are developing programs independently.

The PNW colleges and universities listed on the **Campus Pride Index** chart below have asked to be ranked on their progress on LGBTQIA+ issues. 5 stars is the top ranking given in the Index, and the goal toward which each is working. Not all colleges choose to be ranked by Campus Pride even if they have excellent inclusion programs.

PRIDE Index of Pacific Northwest College Participants*

Five Stars ★★★★★

Portland State University, University of Oregon, Southern Oregon University, University of Washington, Washington State University

Four and a half Stars ★★★★½

Willamette University, CalPoly Humboldt

Four Stars ★★★★

Oregon State University, Gonzaga University, University of Puget Sound, Montana State University, Eastern Washington University

Three and a half Stars ★★★½

Reed College, University of Idaho, North Seattle College, Western Oregon University, Linfield University, University of Alaska Southeast

Three Stars ★★★

Whitman College, College of Idaho, Univ. of Montana

** Index is subject to change over time.*
Check campusprideindex.org for updates

The following are a few samples of various LGBTQAI+ inclusive and supportive programs available at our PNW institutions.

- **University of Alaska (UAF)** promotes diversity and inclusion across the campus and sponsors a **Gender and Sexuality Alliance, Diversity and Action Center** and a **Women, Gender and Sexuality Studies** program.
- **Carroll College's** inclusive housing policy defines itself as a community that embraces respect and inclusivity for all. The **Sexual Orientation and Gender Identity Committee** is a campus community collaborative that cultivates an equitable and safe campus environment through education, awareness, and sociocultural programming.
- **Lewis and Clark College** supports a **Queer Student Union,** a **Queer and Trans Student Association,** and offers inclusive housing in dorms. The College's support system for community members of all sexualities and gender identities provides a safe place for all to express their unique individuality.
- **Oregon Tech** initiated and got funding for a significant **Rainbow Falls Community Coalition** effort to build toward a safer LGBTQ+ community. It addresses issues and provides resources for students, such as the **Safe Zone** program created to provide a more inclusive and accepting campus climate.

- **Pacific Lutheran University's Diversity Center** is committed to caring for PLU community members who identify as LGBTQIA+ and believes that diversity is vital to the vibrancy and sustainability of the university community and our world beyond it. PLU offers inclusive living communities and works with students to address issues of individual need, comfort, and fit.
- **The University of Portland's Gender and Sexuality Partnership's** mission is to build a community that is open and welcoming to students of all sexual orientations. The University sponsors diversity and inclusion programs and events. It offers inclusive housing and a **Mentorship Program** to support all first year students with their transitions to college.
- **Seattle University** is guided by respect for and affirmation of the student's gender identity or expression, prioritizes students' physical safety and emotional health, and has abundant on-campus programming, affinity groups, and a proactive **Office of Diversity and Inclusion.**
- **Western Washington** University's LGBTQ+Western program engages the campus community with transformational knowledge, resources, advocacy, and celebration. Its **Women, Gender and Sexuality** and **Queer Studies** programs offer multi-disciplinary courses and there are gender-neutral facilities and PRIDE housing.

Seminar Class

Saint Martin's University

Lacey, Washington / www. stmartin.edu

This diverse and professional career-oriented University offers strong engineering, nursing, computer science, and education programs and promotes inclusivity, intercultural understanding, social justice, and social responsibility.

Location

Located fifty miles south of Seattle at the south end of picturesque Puget Sound, Lacey is a popular and growing residential and commercial suburb of 55,000 within the larger metro area of Olympia, the state capital of Washington. Olympia is a regional center for the arts, and Lacey is a designated **Green Power Community** for its use of renewable energy sources.

Lacey has 29 city parks, plus natural areas and open spaces. The Pacific Northwest Coast's temperate climate means rain in winter, but not much snow, and pleasantly warm summers.

Community

Saint Martin's strong sense of community is rooted in its Catholic Benedictine Mission to unite academic rigor and excellence with moral thought and social responsibility. The community comes together by learning to live a meaningful life through serving and promoting the common good. One of the most diverse higher education institutions in the PNW, the student population represents twenty different faiths and nineteen different nationalities within the close-knit undergraduate student population of 1400.

Over a third of students are the first in their families to attend college and twenty percent are from out of state. About forty-five percent of students identify as Catholic. Each year a small cohort of students are selected as Benedictine Scholars based on their leadership, academic records, and contributions to the life of their school or faith communities. These students then become mentors to the following year's cohort of scholars after their first year.

The wooded 380 acre campus boasts a new state of the art industrial engineering building with LEED Platinum certification, a new professional foundry and specialized lab facilities for student research in engineering and computer science, and new clinical facilities for nursing. The **Diversity and Equity Center** fosters an inclusive and equitable learning environment inspired by the Benedictine tradition of honoring the dignity of each person. The Center facilitates and promotes inclusivity, intercultural understanding, and social justice.

Academics

Saint Martin University's career preparation is a well-designed four year process that produces excellent results. The academic programs are divided into four divisions, the Hal and Inge Marcus School of Engineering, The College of Education and Counseling, the School of Business, and the College of Arts and Science. The new facilities for Nursing, Civil and Mechanical Engineering, Computer Science/ Information Technology and STEM studies have enhanced these historically strong professional programs. The University's location in a state capital and on the Puget Sound coast offers a wide array of internship options and field training in all disciplines.

The engineering program offers a unique opportunity to get global experience by studying at the University of Technology in Sydney, Australia, during the first semester of sophomore year and still stay on track for graduation in either mechanical or civil engineering.

A recent 2.2 mil grant will increase the number of nursing students from diverse backgrounds seeking B.N. degrees. The grant is providing more financial aid and adding faculty and mentors for students who will be studying and practicing in the new science wing designed for and dedicated to nursing studies and hands-on practical training. Small classes and a good student/faculty ratio provide ample support and encouragement for students. Rigorous teacher education courses stress practicum work with local schools and flexible and integrated programs of study toward certification.

The **SMU Center for Scholarship and Teaching** is noted for nurturing a culture of innovation within the faculty and encourages student/faculty collaboration on research projects. The Center's activities and research are focused on developing the capacity for transformative pedagogy and student mentorship among the Saint Martin's faculty.

Recreational Activities and Residential Life

The **Charneski Recreation Center** includes three multi-purpose courts, a three-lane running track, batting cages, a 9000 sq. ft. fitness center, and an aerobics-dance studio. The University has seven women's and six men's NCAA DII teams, including golf and soccer. SMU's athletes often gain All-Academic honors in the Great Northwest Athletic Conference. The **Outdoor Recreation Center** offers outdoor adventure. Boundless water and mountain sports are easily accessible for St Martin's students, including Mount Rainer and Olympic National Parks.

Student activities include many professional and identity-focused clubs and organizations including a highly competitive Debate Team, Beekeeping Club, Circle K service club, Engineers without Borders, Honor Societies, and a Gender and Sexuality Alliance. The elected student government is active in leadership, student advocacy, and service.

All first year students begin their residential community life in Parsons Hall, which features the typical amenities of a computer lab, community kitchen, conference room, and social and study lounges for 250 students. Two other residences have apartment style living. The food service offers healthy and varied selections.

Financial Aid

The **Act Six** scholarship program is full tuition, full need for students who live in the area and are passionate about social justice and community service. 100% of U.S. students receive some level of financial aid. Work study and student employment often allay some student expenses.

Study Away

SMU abroad opportunities include the **North China Institution for Aerospace Engineering** and an **Irish American Scholars** program. SMU students can study at the **University of Oregon's GEO site in Spain.** They can also take advantage of the engineering department's innovative program in Sydney, Australia.

SMU also has an **Ambassadors Abroad** cultural exchange program for a two week immersion experience in Asian countries. **Benedictine Scholars** receive $10,000 scholarships for four years.

Engineers WithoutBorders

Student chapters of the volunteer organization **Engineers without Borders** are active at ten of our Pacific Northwest colleges and universities. Student and professional engineer volunteers from these chapters donate their time, engineering skills, and professional knowledge to help communities in the U.S. and around the world develop the infrastructure and technology to sustainably meet their basic human needs.

The EWB organization sponsors grant-funded challenge competitions for teams. These encourage the innovative design of cheap and reliable technologies and infrastructures for providing energy, water, heat, refrigeration, and other vital needs to off-grid and endangered communities.

Students can also volunteer to work on new or ongoing engineering projects in all corners of the world and on domestic projects run by the **Community Engineering Corps.**

These projects give chapter members valuable experience with hands-on research and working as part of an engineering team. Student volunteers report benefitting from the personal and professional growth, broadened awareness, and expanded opportunities they gain from their volunteer experiences and EWB chapter involvement.

Saint Martin's University Basic Statistics

Undergraduate Enrollment	Freshman Class Enrollment	Institution Total Enrollment	Female/Male Student Ratio	Female/Male Faculty Ratio	Student/ Faculty Ratio
1,291	242	1,536	59/41	51/49	11/1
# of 1st Year Applications	**# of 1st Year Women Admitted**	**# of 1st Year Men Admitted**	**# of Transfer Students Admitted**	**Overall Yield**	**% of Out-of-State Students**
2,653	1,300	598	284	18%	20%
% Students Living in Campus Housing	**Fraternity/ Sorority Participation**	**% Students Receiving Need-based Aid**	**1st Year Students Retention Rate**	**% Classes Under 30**	**% Caucasian/ White Faculty**
44%	0	75%	80%	99%	89%
# Caucasian / White Students	**# Hispanic / Latinx Students**	**# Asian Students**	**# Black Students**	**# American Indian/ Alaskan, Hawaiian /Native Pacific Islander**	**# International Students**
518	286	129	78	74	21
In-State Tuition and Fees	**Room and Board**	**Out-of-State Tuition and Fees**	**Honors Program Cost**	**Honors Program Grant**	**Athletic Division**
$42,220	$13,390	$42,220	n/a	n/a	NCAA II

Notes:

Seattle University

Seattle, Washington / www. seattleu.edu

Larger and more comprehensive than most private Pacific Northwest Universities, Seattle U offers a vibrant urban experience, holistic education, and a clear community engagement and service mission based on Jesuit principles.

Location

Seattle, the largest city in the Pacific Northwest, is one of the fastest growing in the U.S. It is an oceanic port situated on a hilly isthmus between Puget Sound and Lake Washington and is also home to major companies such as Boeing, Microsoft, and Amazon and an ever-expanding list of newer tech companies. The city is gradually growing in diversity and is a notable hub for global health organizations.

Seattle is a regional center for the visual and performing arts and a historic incubator of successful popular musical groups. The city has earned the title of "fittest city in the U.S." It is also famous for its many artisan coffeehouses, its more than a hundred theater companies, and equal number of art galleries. Seattle's street cars and light rail make it convenient to get around the downtown area. Sea-Tac International airport serves both the Seattle metro area and the nearby city of Tacoma. The climate is Mediterranean with cool, wet winters and mild dry summers.

Pike Place Market, Seattle, WA

Community

This Jesuit Catholic University's commitment to inclusivity and accessibility for all students is clearly stated. With 4000 undergraduates and 3000 graduate students, the attractive 90 acre campus serves as a happily busy urban sanctuary.

The **Center for Community Engagement** fosters strong connections between students, staff, faculty, and the city's government, schools, and community-based organizations.

Three out of four students participate in place-based service learning, research, and leadership programs that focus on advancing social changes toward a more just and humane world.

Seattle University is also relatively diverse, with only 52% of students identifying as white and about 60% coming from out of state. Less than a quarter of students are Catholic, and 12% are of various non-Christian religions.

Academics

Seattle U describes its learning objectives as holistic, focusing on education of the whole person in support of professional goals development and leadership empowerment. The faculty members are known as both scholars and teachers of high quality. Most Seattle U classes are surprisingly small, and students report that they are happy with the level of care and attention they receive from faculty.

The two most popular programs at SU are in the Business and Health Professions fields, which attract 30% of students. Nursing at SU is among the top programs in the U.S. Visual and Performing Arts-related majors are chosen by about 8% of students. The University offers a uniquely flexible B.A. in Interdisciplinary Arts with a Specialization in Arts Leadership. The music department's curriculum is designed not only to attract students but to place emphasis on developing young talent.

The **Albers School of Business and Economics** offers eleven concentrations, a leadership development program, and a **Mentor Program** linked to the Seattle business community. The **College of Science and Engineering** offers more than a dozen STEM majors. These courses provide substantial lab experience and opportunities for undergraduate research, year-long industry sponsored **Senior Projects** for engineering and computer students, and humanitarian engineering projects in other countries. **Communication and Media** is another popular and very flexible program focused on written and spoken communication, visual and digital skills development, and experiential learning through internships with Seattle companies and organizations. The placement rate of graduates into jobs is also outstanding.

Recreational Activities and Residential Life

The **Redhawk Center** and **Eisiminger Fitness Center** facilities offer comprehensive recreational, fitness, and athletic space, including two 6-lane swimming pools and men's and women's saunas. Intramural Sports and Sports Clubs give various play options, and the Outdoors program offers group trips, equipment, and adventures. Eight men's and ten women's varsity teams compete at NCAA Division I level.

Clubs and organizations run the gamut at Seattle U. The **Student Events and Activities Council** has a weekly schedule of social events and the many cultural group activities and performing arts plays and concerts on campus.

Seattle U offers a wide variety of residential options, but most first and second year students live in one of the traditional dorms where floors are coed, and each building has a kitchen, lounge, and study areas. The residences have supportive **Theme Communities** designed to make immediate connections with new friends. International students, and those interested in global studies and cross-cultural education, gravitate to the Xavier Global House living/learning community. Multiple Campus dining venues offer food for every diet. Older students can move to on-campus apartments and nearby apartment complexes off campus that are leased for Seattle U students. Housing is gender inclusive. Most residence halls have either a Jesuit in Residence or a Resident Minister in addition to the staff.

Financial Aid

About 92% of Seattle U undergrads receive some form of financial aid. Merit scholarships are available and include a major **Leadership Award,** a **Fostering Scholars** scholarship for students who have been in foster care, and designated scholarships for STEM majors.

Study Away

About five hundred SU students participate in study abroad programs each year. The **Education Abroad** office offers a vast list of SU-sponsored opportunities to explore and assists students with planning and course credit information. Some departments offer specific study abroad programs as well as faculty-led options.

Fostered Youth

Many colleges and universities have designed scholarship plans for previously fostered youth. These students have access to modest Federal Government support through the **John H. Chafee Foster Care Independence Program** for youth who have been in foster care.

The federal program offers Education and Training Vouchers (ETVs) to help meet those youth's post-secondary education and training needs. This funding also applies to former foster youth who were adopted or entered into guardianship after their 13th birthday.

Youth can access the ETG vouchers for a maximum of five years.

Amounts of ETG awards are based on FAFSA verification and on remaining financial need after any Pell grant award and after any state grants are subtracted.

Most states have a centralized Chafee application process and annual update program.

Students must notify the college financial aid office of their eligibility. The grant should then be included in the financial aid package prepared by the institution.

Seattle University Basic Statistics

Undergraduate Enrollment	Freshman Class Enrollment	Institution Total Enrollment	Female/Male Student Ratio	Female/Male Faculty Ratio	Student/ Faculty Ratio
4,301	289	7,268	62/38	55/43	11/1
# of 1st Year Applications	**# of 1st Year Women Admitted**	**# of 1st Year Men Admitted**	**# of Transfer Students Admitted**	**Overall Yield**	**% of Out-of-State Students**
8,539	4742	2,270	899	14%	55%
% Students Living in Campus Housing	**Fraternity/ Sorority Participation**	**% Students Receiving Need-based Aid**	**1st Year Students Retention Rate**	**% Classes Under 30**	**% Caucasian/ White Faculty**
49%	0	56%	85%	80%	75%
# Caucasian / White Students	**# Hispanic / Latinx Students**	**# Asian Students**	**# Black Students**	**# American Indian/ Alaskan, Hawaiian /Native Pacific Islander**	**# International Students**
1,596	616	976	191	65	370
In-State Tuition and Fees	**Room and Board**	**Out-of-State Tuition and Fees**	**Honors Program Cost**	**Honors Program Grant**	**Athletic Division**
$51,275	$12,524	$51,274	0	$1800	NCAA Div.I

Notes:

Whitman College

Walla Walla, Washington / www.Whitman.edu

Whitman's reputation as one of the finest liberal arts colleges in the nation is based on its rigorous academics, outstanding faculty, and creative and deeply engaged students.

Location

Walla Walla is home to more than 120 wineries with tasting rooms and a nationally recognized culinary scene focusing on farm-to-table dishes emphasizing Walla Walla's agricultural roots. The city is home to the world's largest contemporary fine arts foundry, where many of the twenty-three remarkable installations on the Whitman campus's popular Sculpture Walk were cast. With 260 days of sunshine a year and a mild, dry climate, Walla Walla offers an abundance of outdoor recreation opportunities.

Walla Walla, WA

Some of the finest restaurants in Walla Walla often have to be booked well in advance. Still there are many fun eating spots for student budgets, plus theaters, handsome historic buildings, three colleges, and a very upbeat vibe in this artsy southeast Washington city.

Community

Whitman is a supportive scholarly community that encourages creativity and offers experiences that help develop ethical and meaningful lives. Like many PNW institutions, Whitman struggles to become more racially and ethnically diverse. However, ten percent of Whitman's students come from other countries and 64% from out of State. Whitman is a **Davis United World Colleges Scholars** partner which brings highly qualified UWC graduates to the college from many other countries. Students tend to form community through involvement in clubs, sports, Greek life, or friendships with other members of their residence halls.

The **Glover Alston Center s**erves as a place where conversations about diversity and social justice occur and clubs and organizations can meet. The college hires student leaders to lead **Community Engagement Programs** that facilitate student volunteer opportunities in Walla Walla.

Each year the college adopts a new theme to deepen collective understanding of a critical issue, such as *Climate Reckoning, Climate Justice*. By encouraging theme-based discussion across courses and with special programs during the year, the college community learns and explores together and thus gains a collective understanding of the dimensions of the problems and the range of possible responses.

Academics

All Whitman first year students take a two-semester seminar series that offers innovative teaching and intriguing topics. The spring seminar focuses on giving students experience in persuasive arguments based on research-based evidence. The **Center for Writing and Speaking** provides resources and opportunities for students who need further help developing these proficiencies.

One of the few disadvantages of a small college with small classes is that some faculty gain such popularity that students complain it can be challenging to get into their classes, even though the 8/1 student to faculty ratio is commendable. Over 30% of students graduating in 2020 chose to major in social studies or psychology, followed by 16.4% majoring in biology/life science and 10.8% in the visual and performing arts.

The **Center for Global Studies** is an initiative that has generated team-taught interdisciplinary courses that infuse a global perspective into the curriculum and enriches it by bringing international professionals and visiting scholars to the college through the **O'Donnell Visiting Educator** program. Faculty-student research collaborations are encouraged and supported by awards such as the Faculty-Student Summer Research Awards.

Whitman offers an innovative interdisciplinary program that integrates concepts from biology, chemistry, and physics and has a partnership with the **Infectious Disease Research Institute,** which supports two students to gain paid experience in a biotechnology organization. Whitman has a **Phi Beta Kappa** chapter that celebrates its highest achieving students.

Recreational Activities and Residential Life

Whitman has seven residence halls and eleven special-interest houses. Students are required to live on campus for four semesters. Students seem to agree residential life is a pleasant and fun learning/living experience that fosters long-term friendships. Gender-inclusive housing is available and accommodating. The **Interest Houses** are considered prime choices and include the **Writing House,** which has traditions such as a weekly **Writer's Colony**, and a coffeehouse evening of student performances. The college also owns unfurnished off-campus houses for older student groups. Greek life attracts about twenty percent of the student population.

Students are actively involved in a wide range of clubs and organizations, from academic and identity themes to issue-based, arts-related, and professions-relevant groups, plus twelve club sports groups. Outdoor recreation is a major outlet and the **Whitman Events Board** is a student managed committee that organizes fun events and brings music and entertainment to the campus. Whitman is proud of their scholar-athletes who compete at NCAA DIV III in seven sports. About 17% of students participate in at least one varsity sport. Recreation and sports facilities are large and well equipped.

Financial Aid

Whitman offers an **Early Financial Aid Guarantee** allowing prospective students to see what their financial aid award covers before applying. The college guarantees full tuition will be covered by scholarships and grants to admitted students from Washington State whose families earn less than $80,000 a year.

Whitman Merit scholarships are generous. There are also talent scholarships in visual and performing arts and debate.

Study Away

Forty-five percent of Whitman students take advantage of off-campus studies. **Crossroads** courses are faculty-led short term opportunities offered in summer or during breaks. These can range from studying Plant Biology in Sweden to Culture, Politics and Ecology studies in China.

Semester and year programs range from SEA Education in Woods Hole, MA, to affiliated programs with other colleges such as Syracuse University in Florence for art history and architecture to a Year of Study in Munich managed by Lewis and Clark College and myriad others through international study organizations.

United World Colleges

United World Colleges (UWC) consists of eighteen schools and colleges on four continents. The majority of them focus on the 16-19 age group, with some also catering to younger students.

Each school has a unique location and character and is dedicated to nurturing young people's energy and idealism into empathy, responsibility and lifelong action.

At these schools, students aged 16-19 study the **International Baccalaureate Diploma** Program. This Diploma can qualify them for university study around the world. Eighty percent of UWC students receive some level of financial aid.

Through partnerships with universities and higher education institutions such as Whitman, UWC offers their graduates opportunities to further their education beyond UWC.

These partnerships provide unique access for UWC graduates to some of the world's leading universities and are testimony to the high caliber of UWC graduates.

Whitman College Basic Statistics

Undergraduate Enrollment	Freshman Class Enrollment	Institution Total Enrollment	Female/Male Student Ratio	Female/Male Faculty Ratio	Student/ Faculty Ratio
1,559	477	1,559	56/44	47/53	9/1
# of 1st Year Applications	**# of 1st Year Women Admitted**	**# of 1st Year Men Admitted**	**# of Transfer Students Admitted**	**Overall Yield**	**% of Out-of-State Students**
5,274	1,883	1,156	56	16%	64%
% Students Living in Campus Housing	**Fraternity/ Sorority Participation**	**% Students Receiving Need-based Aid**	**1st Year Students Retention Rate**	**% Classes Under 30**	**% Caucasian/ White Faculty**
67%	12% / 11%	45%	89.46%	93%	88%
# Caucasian / White Students	**% Hispanic / Latinx Students**	**# Asian Students**	**# Black Students**	**# American Indian/ Alaskan, Hawaiian /Native Pacific Islander**	**# International Students**
961	141	95	37	10	159
In-State Tuition and Fees	**Room and Board**	**Out-of-State Tuition and Fees**	**Honors Program Cost**	**Honors Program Grant**	**Athletic Division**
$58,600	$14,210	$58,600	n/a	n/a	NCAA III

Notes:

In Focus: Visual and Performing Arts

Departmental offerings in the visual and performing arts are found at almost every liberal arts-based college and university, even though the percentage of students graduating with a major in one of these fields is relatively small.

Higher education institutions recognize that the arts are popular extracurricular activities for students and that their campus communities are deeply enriched by opportunities for engagement with and exposure to the arts. Even our most STEM-oriented colleges and universities support creative talents and encourage creation, practice, and entrepreneurship in the arts.

One of three Oregon Shakespeare Festival theaters in Ashland, OR

The experience of creating and performing in demanding and collaborative settings develops interpretive and functional skills, broadens cultural and social knowledge, and encourages innovative problem solving, all critical capacities for future success and self-fulfillment in life.

Most programs welcome non-majors as participants in arts activities. They offer interesting and fun elective classes in the arts that will not only improve individual skills and talents but could lead to discovering new outlets and modalities for creative expression. Those considering a professional career in the arts will want to explore programs that offer considerable depth and breadth in their curricular options, sufficient numbers of professionally recognized and student-engaged faculty, excellent facilities, and collaborative connections with other arts organizations.

Here you will find a sampling of the many and varied visual and performing arts programs offered at our Pacific Northwest colleges and institutions. Many of these offer competitive scholarships even for talented students not majoring in the arts.

Institution	Performing Arts Program
Southern Oregon University	**SOU's Oregon Center for the Arts** is a vibrant home for creatives of all arts disciplines. Its theater program is a designated Center of Excellence in the Fine and Performing Arts. It offers pre-professional training and B.S./B.A. degrees in Music Industry and Production Studies, a Master's program in Theater Studies and an MBA in Arts Management. A full calendar of campus-based productions and ensemble performances draws audiences from around the region. You can carve your own path in the **Emerging Media and Digital Arts** Department or focus in any art medium in the University's **Visual Arts Complex**. The Music department boasts world class artist-teachers who emphasize individual exploration and creative collaboration. Students enjoy a superb **Chamber Music Series** and the city's renowned **Oregon Shakespeare Festival** regional repertory company's ten-month season in one outdoor and two indoor theaters.

Institution	Performing Arts Program
University of Puget Sound	The **School of Music** at UPS offers a wide range of amateur and conservatory level courses and ensembles, including jazz, open to all students. It also provides professional guidance for those interested in careers in musical performance, scholarship, and teaching. UPS's **Schneebeck Concert Hall** hosts musical events throughout the year. The UPS Theater program is collaborative and adventurous, has an endowed **Guest Artist Workshop** program, and ties to the Seattle theater community. Its **ARTBARN**'s innovative summer residency program offers internships for UPS theater students.
Pacific University	Pacific University's rigorous 5 year **Bachelor of Music Therapy** program (BMT) includes both a practicum and a 6-9 month Internship and prepares students for professional Board Certification. At the undergraduate level, the University offers degrees in music, music education, instrumental performance, piano performance, and vocal performance. Ensembles include Jazz, Concert Choir, Philharmonic Orchestra, Chamber Ensembles, and a Symphonic Band.
College of Idaho	C of I has impressive performance spaces that host not only student concerts and productions but also those of the **Caldwell Fine Arts** association for the Treasure Valley region. These include a black box theater, 200 seat recital hall, an 850 seat proscenium house, and an outdoor amphitheater. Music students benefit from instruction by members of the renowned **Langroise Chamber Music Trio**, a resident artist ensemble, along with other gifted and diverse faculty. Theater students compete annually in the **Kennedy Center American College Theater Festival**. The **Boise Symphony, McCarter Theater Center,** and **Boise Contemporary Theater** offer internship opportunities, as do Caldwell Fine Arts and various regional festivals.
University of Washington	UW's fine and performing arts programs are well-known for innovation and interdisciplinary perspectives. In 2022 UW began long-overdue renovations and additions to the **Music and Art, Art History,** and **Design** facilities. The **School of Drama**, with numerous performance venues and study and design facilities, requires a holistic mix of acting, tech, history, and literature. Advanced management, directing, and internship experiences are available for those concentrating in performance, design, or drama. The department has close ties with the vibrant Seattle theater community. UW's flexible and highly regarded **Dance** program offers major and minor degrees. The **UW Symphony** is a national prize winner, and the music faculty is outstanding. The new **BA in Ethnomusicology** degree option reflects increased student interest in global musical explorations in diversity, equity, inclusion, and cultural contexts of music and offers flexible opportunities for independent musical study.
Whitman College	Whitman's well-endowed Guest Artist program brings prominent working professionals to the campus to share their expertise and experience. The Harper Joy Theater has been enhanced by a seven million dollar renovation and technical upgrade with an additional Studio Theater and costume shop. All students, regardless of major, are welcome to participate in the theater, dance, and musical productions and courses. The Hall of Music boasts a 300 seat recital hall, electronic music studio, thirty music faculty and instructors to work with, and seven performing ensembles. The Art Department offers an interdisciplinary concentration in **Visual Culture Studies** and a prominent faculty of working artists.

Institution	Performing Arts Program
University of Montana	**UM's College of the Arts and Media** supports vibrant programs from film to e-sport gaming and music, theater and dance. Extensive facilities include cutting-edge equipment, extensive studio spaces, and material-specific workshops. Six major dance concerts are produced annually. The Music department fosters city-campus collaboration and performance opportunities. The Montana Repertory Theater, for instance, offers students opportunities to gain professional experience.
Boise State University	Boise State's **School for the Arts** includes an interdisciplinary department of **Theater, Film, and Creative Writing** and encourages experiential learning such as a **Narrative Television Initiative**. The Creative Writing program publishes the **Idaho Review** and a **Free Poetry Chapbook** series. Boise's music department supports one of the premier wind bands in the Northwest, along with numerous other ensembles and a full calendar of concerts and recitals. Its **Morrison Center for the Performing Arts** includes a 2000 seat hall used not only by Boise departments but also by the **Boise Opera** and **Boise Philharmonic**, which offer internships.
University of Oregon	UO's comprehensive fine and performing arts options include the **College of Design,** with art, art and technology, art history, product design, and architecture degrees, the **School of Music and Dance,** with seven majors and multiple concentrations, and a Department of Theater Arts. UO's **Repertory Dance Company** tours throughout the state and enjoys the sprung floors in four dance studios and the 250 seat **Dougherty Dance Theater**. The **School of Music** is considered the premier music program in the Pacific Northwest, has the largest full time music faculty, strongly supports creation of new work, and presents about 300 concerts each year, many at the University's 520 seat **Beal Concert Hall**. The Collegium Musicum early music ensemble uses the university's collection of historic instruments. Tracks exist for performing and composing artists, industry-focused students, and those interested in music business or journalism.
Willamette University	A recent merger with **Pacific Northwest College of Art** enhances Willamette's fine arts, design, and visual studies. This downtown Portland college houses the **Center for Contemporary Art & Culture** with exhibitions, lectures, performances, and publication programs, and the **Museum of Contemporary Craft** collection. On the Salem campus, the **Mary Stuart Rogers Music Center** supports a Chamber orchestra, Jazz and Wind Ensembles, and several vocal groups, many of which tour regularly. Music production facilities include a 15 workstation **Digital Music Studio** and a recording studio. An innovative **New Music Series** is directed by the college's **Composer in Residence.**

Willamette University

Salem, Oregon / www.willamette.edu

Students with varied interests are attracted to this innovative and historic University because it offers accelerated degrees, two city campuses, and expanded opportunities in global and interdisciplinary studies and in the professional creative arts.

Location

Salem, population 178,000, is the capital city of Oregon. The city is 47 miles south of Portland and only an hour from the Cascade Mountains to the east and the Pacific Ocean beaches to the west. Climate is warm and temperate, with rain and a little snow in winter and mainly dry summers.

Salem has numerous parks, a good trail system, busy downtown shopping area, a riverfront park, and pleasant established neighborhoods. Many residents are employed at various state government offices and agencies in the city, which, along with the business sector, offer excellent opportunities for internships.

Community

As the first university to be established in Oregon, Willamette has a long and distinguished history of community involvement. The University's evocative motto "Not Unto Ourselves Alone are We Born" is put into practice by service learning options which include a Service Saturdays program, and incorporates experiential service learning into courses that require students to engage in projects with community partners.

Students describe Willamette as a close-knit and friendly community with excellent relationships among students, staff, and faculty. About 71% of its 1868 students come from out of state. The University is recognized for its strong support of first generation and low income students which has resulted in timely graduation rates and career success. Over a third of Willamette students are students of color.

A recent merger with the **Pacific Northwest College of the Arts (PNCA)** has diversified and increased the student population, added a Portland campus, and enhanced and expanded the University's fine arts curricula.

College Farm Stand Shopping

Academics

The **College of Arts and Sciences** offers more than fifty majors and programs. Many of these are distinctly interdisciplinary and provide experiential learning through internships, fieldwork and lab projects, and a wide array of undergraduate research opportunities. The 10:1 student to faculty ratio keeps class sizes small and allows for excellent student-faculty engagement and mentorship.

PNCA courses have added a wide range of art and craft course options for Willamette students. On the Willamette campus the music program has an excellent reputation. It sponsors vocal and instrumental ensembles that perform and tour regionally and an experimental New Music series.

Social sciences and psychology are popular majors for 30% of Willamette graduates. Political science, history, and policy majors have easy access to state government internships, and fifty percent of students complete internships sometime during their years at Willamette. The University provides a substantial number of research grants for scholarly, creative, investigative, and professional projects.

Willamette's well-regarded law, business management, and data science graduate schools enable Willamette to offer students the advantages of accelerated degree programs that save students money and time. One combines a BA and MBA with just five years of study, another earns dual undergraduate and law degrees in six years, and a third offers BS/MS dual degrees in four years and one summer.

The University offers degrees in Global Cultural Studies, International Studies, Latin American Studies, Asian Studies, and study in five languages. Willamette has a close affiliation with **Tokyo International University.** This relationship results in extensive study abroad opportunities. Willamette hosts a small American co-campus of TIU on the Willamette U campus and offers language and cultural exchange experiences for students from both programs.

Recreational Activities and Residential Life

First and second year students are required to live on campus. Students have a choice of several residence halls, one of which has a **Global Living/Learning Community** floor, some small houses, and a University Apartment complex. The food service offers healthy food at several cafes, including spacious **Goudy Commons.**

At the Portland campus all first year and transfer students live in furnished apartments at a contemporary student housing complex called **Art House,** just 5 minutes from PNCA's **Arlene and Harold Schnitzler Center for Arts and Design.**

Willamette students can choose from over seventy clubs and organizations, including Native and Indigenous, Black, and Queer Student Unions, and many service clubs. The **Zena Farm Club** is a student run 300 acre organic farm which the **Willamette U Sustainability Institute** also uses for field courses and research.

Willamette has nine men's and eleven women's varsity teams, which compete at the NCAA DIV III level. Facilities for sports and recreation include a field house, fitness center, 2 stadiums, a six lane 25yd competitions pool, sports fields, and tennis courts. Club sports, outdoor recreation activities and trips, and intramural sports options are also popular with students.

Financial Aid

Willamette's generous aid packages combine merit and need-based scholarships for first year and transfer students. There are generous merit scholarships for students who qualify.

Study Away

Willamette sponsors myriad student abroad semester and year-long programs that earn academic credit and about fifty percent of students participate. Summer programs are faculty-led such as the **Willamette U Archeology Field School** on the Orkney Islands of Scotland or one in Quito, Ecuador for intensive Spanish and cultural experience at the **Andean Center for Latin American Studies** in partnership with the University of Portland.

College Farms

Willamette's **Zena Farm Club** is part of a healthy trend of hands-on student-run farms and gardens at colleges around the country. Universities and colleges have found that campus agricultural operations are popular with a generation of students who place high value on locally sourced food and sustainable and organic agriculture.

These farms give students an opportunity to get outside, and plan, plant, and harvest a bounty of fresh food while absorbing essential knowledge about the processes and challenges of organic land management.

Farm programs range from small projects on campus to large acreage operations with full-on farming activities, including raising animals and managing major crops. Many of these operations can provide a substantial amount of fresh food for campus meal services and host farm stands for the community. Some, like Willamette's Zena Farm, are run entirely by students, others have a farm manager.

Most college farms have on-site courses and workshops and provide a field site for sustainable living research. Many are connected to or developed by a department of ecology or agronomy. Some have residential housing for students who want an immersive experience or are involved in research projects.

Willamette University Basic Statistics

Undergraduate Enrollment	Freshman Class Enrollment	Institution Total Enrollment	Female/Male Student Ratio	Female/Male Faculty Ratio	Student/ Faculty Ratio
1,237	259	1,864	56/44	48/52	10/1
# of 1st Year Applications	**# of 1st Year Women Admitted**	**# of 1st Year Men Admitted**	**# of Transfer Students Admitted**	**Overall Yield**	**% of Out-of-State Students**
3,680	1,851	1,070	76	9%	70%
% Students Living in Campus Housing	**Fraternity/ Sorority Participation**	**% Students Receiving Need-based Aid**	**1st Year Students Retention Rate**	**% Classes Under 30**	**% Caucasian/ White Faculty**
57%	16% / 13%	61%	89.46%	97%	80%
# Caucasian / White Students	**# Hispanic / Latinx Students**	**# Asian Students**	**# Black Students**	**# American Indian/ Alaskan, Hawaiian /Native Pacific Islander**	**# International Students**
783	169	64	21	10	25
In-State Tuition and Fees	**Room and Board**	**Out-of-State Tuition and Fees**	**Honors Program Cost**	**Honors Program Grant**	**Athletic Division**
$45,428	$14,240	$45,428	n/a	n/a	NCAA III

Notes:

In Focus: Community College Options

Why consider attending a residential Community College?

A. To achieve affordable 1-2 year technical and applied skills program certifications/degrees that lead to gainful employment with good advancement potential.

B. For affordable completion of General/Core Education course requirements prior to transferring to a four year college or university.

C. To experience residential college community life away from home while still achieving either A. or B.

D. To develop a stronger academic achievement record than shown on the student's high school transcript and therefore improve chances of transfer admission to competitive higher ed institutions.

Weed, CA and Mt. Shasta

Bend, OR with Mt. Bachelor in the background

Good News:

- Almost all colleges and universities lose a certain portion of students during first and second years, so these institutions welcome qualified transfer applicants depending on the number of classroom and program spaces that become available for the upcoming year.
- Most public and private colleges and universities have some form of articulation agreement and/or institutional policies for transfer. These ensure that community college students who follow an established public community college transfer curriculum and earn qualifying grades will be considered for admission with advanced standing.
- Students attending a community college located near a state university campus may be able to take some courses at the university campus while completing others at the community college.
- Students attending a community college in one state may also have options for transferring CC credits to private or public institutions in a different state.
- In every PNW/Cascadia state there are community colleges that offer student housing right on campus.

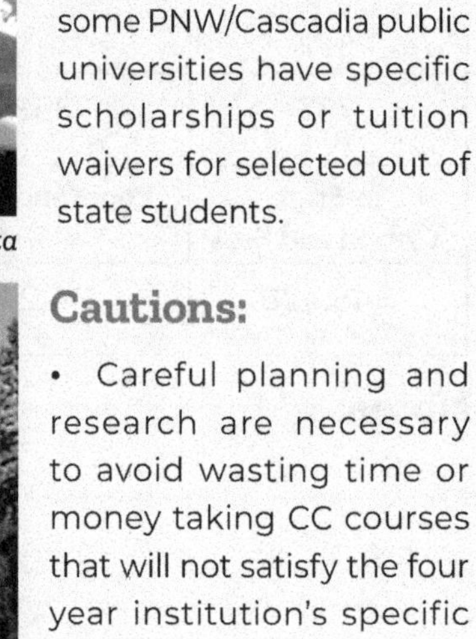

- Many out of state students will have access to the WUE tuition reduction program for both CC and 4 yr. institutions in another state and some PNW/Cascadia public universities have specific scholarships or tuition waivers for selected out of state students.

Cautions:

- Careful planning and research are necessary to avoid wasting time or money taking CC courses that will not satisfy the four year institution's specific requirements for credit transfer.
- Attending a community college in another state does not give you in-state residence for tuition purposes at public universities in that other state if you came into the state solely for education purposes.
- Whether starting at a two year or four year college, students need to adequately research and plan ahead for all financial opportunities and budgetary demands and make decisions accordingly.

College	Description
Central Oregon Community College Bend, OR See the Oregon State University-Cascades Profile for detailed location description.	COCC's new residence hall serves up to 330 students and there are several meal plans from which to choose. The college offers associate degrees in 46 fields including aviation pilot, fire service administration, outdoor leadership and world languages. A degree partnership allows for joint admissions to both COCC and Oregon State University-Cascades.
College of the Redwoods Eureka, California See the Cal Poly Humboldt Profile for detailed location description.	Bordered by the Pacific Ocean and the magnificent Redwood forests, CR offers 37 Associate Degrees with transfer pathways to nearby Cal Poly Humboldt and other CSU's, and to some private colleges, and offers many certificate programs. The campus provides residential living on campus for about 150 students and a dining hall that serves organic produce from the college's own sustainable farm
Missoula College Missoula, Montana See the University of Montana Profile for detailed description	Missoula offers Transformational Learning Opportunities designed to build students' confidence with education and training experiences that provide a foundation for success in a fulfilling career. Certificates and Associates degrees provide a smooth transition into a four year degree at UM. There is on campus housing if desired.
Prince William Sound College, Valdez, Alaska Valdez is on the Alaska Marine Highway and accessible by ferry and air from Juneau and by road and air from Anchorage. *See the UAA, UAF and UAS Profiles for more information on the U Alaska universities.*	As part of the University of Alaska system, Prince William offers direct transfer pathways to any of the three universities in the UA system, as well as transfers to other U.S. universities. Valdez offers rugged mountain and ocean recreation and adventure in a stunning glacier studded landscape. Students are housed in three spacious apartment style furnished housing units. No out of state tuition is charged.
Bellevue College Bellevue, Washington Located just across Lake Washington from Seattle, Bellevue is part of the Seattle metro area.	With a total enrollment of over 14,000, Bellevue is the largest of the 34 Washington state community colleges. It offers some applied bachelor's degrees as well as associate transfer degrees in a multitude of fields, including theater and music. Athletes compete in 11 team sports in the NWAC conference. Bellevue has modern residence halls for 400 students.
North Idaho College Coeur d'Alene Idaho Located on the shore line of the 26 mile long Lake Coeur d'Alene at an elevation of 2100 ft. Coeur d'Alene is a famous recreational resort area with a population of 55,000.	North Idaho College is a comprehensive community college serving 5000 students. The residence hall offers rooms for 198 students with meals in the nearby Student Union Bldg., social and group study lounges, and learning/living activities. It offers a wide array of transfer degree programs. The campus includes the 1100 seat Shuler Performing Arts Center, a wellness and recreation center, team recreational sports, and varsity teams that compete in five sports in the NWAC conference.

College	Description
College of the Siskiyous Weed, California The 250 acre campus is located at 3400 ft. elevation in the California mountains near the Oregon/California border and at the base of 14,000 ft. Mount Shasta and its ski area. *The Oregon Exchange is a reciprocity agreement that includes in state tuition for eligible transfer students looking to attend SOU or OIT and allows Oregon residents to attend College of the Siskiyous at a discounted rate.*	The Lodges at College of the Siskiyous provide community living for 164 students in two buildings. There is a required meal plan. The college offers numerous transfer programs and CTE training programs. The campus has a 562 seat theater and a gym. Outdoor recreation, and water and mountain sports abound. Varsity athletes compete in 8 sports in the Golden Valley Conference. The College has a reciprocal agreement with Oregon Tech and Southern Oregon University.
Treasure Valley Community College Ontario, Oregon Ontario is a small city in the Eastern Oregon's Treasure Valley region at an elevation of 2150,' less than an hour from the city of Boise, ID. TVCC is located on the Snake River at the Idaho border.	A Cultural and Performing Arts Center and 8 varsity sports teams, including rodeo, enliven this campus of 3000 students. The Residence Hall offers coed living for 142 students in double and single suites and a meal plan. There are AA and AS degree direct transfer partnerships with Oregon public institutions and with the nearby private College of Idaho.

Jedediah Smith Redwoods State Park, N. California

Community College Transfer

Many residential and non-residential community colleges are in close proximity to a four year college, or university, in the same area. Many of these neighboring institutions collaborate closely, even sharing campus housing and some facilities. Other community colleges operate as a division of a state university system. Some four year institutions have developed special transfer agreements with specific community colleges in their region. In whatever way they are configured, these collaborations will usually provide enhanced options for transfer, and sometimes dual enrollment opportunities, for students who begin at the partner community college.

All state universities welcome qualified students from their own state community colleges and adhere to established transfer agreements. Transferring from one state's community college to a state university in another state is possible, but may have course and program credit limitations, and out of state tuition is usually, although not always, higher. Careful research and planning into options and potential restrictions in transferring is recommended in order not to waste credits and money. For both in-state and out of state transfer options, check out the Transfer section on the four year institution's website. This will provide information on which course credits will transfer, and on whether a certain grade in that course is required in order to transfer.

A Collaboration of White Pelicans—Klamath Lake, Southern Oregon/California Border region.

Southern Oregon/Northern California Region

Here are just a few community colleges and four year institutions that have strong mutual relationships.

Southern Oregon University ⟷ College the Siskiyous ⟷ Oregon Technical Institute

City of Bend, Oregon

- Central Oregon Community College
- Oregon State University Cascades

City of Missoula, Montana

- Montana Technical Institute
- Missoula College

Eastern Oregon and Western Border Idaho Region

- Treasure Valley Community College
- College of Idaho
- Boise State Universit

Arcata/Eureka California Community

- College of the Redwoods
- Cal Poly Humboldt

For further information see page 147: In Focus - Career and Technology Education Options

Northwest Washington Region

- Western Washington University
- Olympic College
- Peninsula Community College

Seattle skyline and Mt Rainier on a clear day.

SECTION TWO

Public Universities and Colleges

Private versus Public Higher Education Cost Differences

Our Pacific Northwest public universities, like those in other regions, receive some degree of supplemental funding from both state and federal government sources. This is why tuition at public universities is lower than at private institutions.

However, at both private and public institutions students who qualify as low-income can access federal government assistance to help with higher education costs.

The Pell and SEOG grants are available to low-income U.S. students studying in the U.S. In Canada similar grants for Canadian students are called Bursaries. The U.S. government also offers Direct Federal Education Loans to students studying either in the U.S. or in Canada.

Most U.S. states also provide additional, if limited, support for their in-state students through state education opportunity grants. Although each U.S. state differs in its ability and enthusiasm for funding higher education, such public state-based funding does keep higher education and training more affordable for many students.

The good news is that private college costs can be surprisingly competitive through generous offers of merit aid and need-based financial assistance, for those students they want to enroll. Such financial aid offers can come close to matching what a student would pay at a home-state public institution.

Our Regional State Universities

Our smaller regional state universities have a basic mission of meeting the education and workforce training needs of their home region's communities and economies. These institutions are generally accessible to a wide range of students. They have a greater emphasis on supportive instruction and training of students at the undergraduate level than the research universities. Nonetheless, both types of institutions put a high value on teaching.

The regional state universities also tend to have smaller classes, more students who commute from the local area, and distinct academic programs that relate to their local region's environmental, cultural, and economic assets and priorities.

Our Public Institutes of Technology

Technology institutes primarily focus on training for specific careers in Applied STEM (*science, technology, engineering, and math*), including medical technologies, management, communication, applied psychology, and other applied professions. Advanced math courses are required in many engineering and tech programs.

Tech institutes have a strong emphasis on experiential learning, co-op, internship, and on the job experiences. They also maintain close relationships with the industries, organizations, businesses, and public agencies that eagerly recruit their well-trained and work-ready graduates.

Our Public Research Universities

There is at least one public research university in each state. Their mission is not only to provide affordable access to effective education and training for the 21st century workforce but also to provide the space and means for faculty scholars to engage in significant research in their fields.

These research universities often serve as anchors for collaborative efforts among institutions, community partners, government agencies, and private industry to address national and global concerns, protect critical assets, and map effective pathways that enhance economic equity and inclusivity.

Public research universities are usually quite large, with many more lecture style classes. They also attract a variety of institutes and centers of critical research and advocacy that provide ambitious students with good options for participating in a research team.

The research universities also have well established graduate programs at the master's and doctorate levels in many departments. Graduate students at these large universities will often have teaching assistant (TA) duties as well.

Honors colleges and honors programs at larger universities consist of a cohort of top achieving students who are offered small, more challenging, seminar-type classes taught by professors, instead of the usual general education courses.

Large research institutions are also likely to have varsity sports teams that compete at Division I level and a devoted following among the students and alumni of the university.

Using Research and Comparison

The **College Research and Comparison Workshop** offered at the start of this guide can help you decide if you are self-directed enough to handle large class sizes, can study independently, and have a strong passion for a specific academic field. If this is your learning style, you should explore your options at large research universities to see if you can find a close match to your criteria and career goals.

However, if you want more time to explore several areas of interest before declaring a major; and learn better in smaller classes with more individual faculty support, then you should look further. Study regional state universities, technical institutes, private colleges, and the Honors Colleges at research universities, to find the closest matches for your personal criteria and expectations for a fun and productive college experience.

Should You Use a Net Price Calculator?

Net Price Calculators are a tool that is available on many college and university websites. These allow prospective students to get an estimate of tuition and fees and room and board, based on their personal data. Most higher education institutions offer this online tool, but there is a lot of variation in what questions they ask and how they weigh that information.

Nonetheless, using a Net Price Calculator can give you a general idea of the difference between the advertised "sticker price" of a college and what discount an institution may offer. Use it to compare several institutions in terms of the difference there is between sticker price and estimated price for you at various institutions.

Some of the questions are similar to what is asked on the FAFSA. Make sure the college's tuition data is current, not based on earlier years, since costs can rise by several percentage points over time.

Also, the FAFSA application for 2022-23 will be considerably changed from previous years, so net price calculators on college websites will have to update their systems to take these changes into account.

So yes, use the Net Price Calculators, but remember they only give a very general estimate, never a promise.

University of Alaska Anchorage

Anchorage, Alaska / www.uaa.alaska.edu

The unique combination of big city location, arctic and global industry field research options, and a desire for cultural diversity, attracts students to UAA from around Alaska and other states and countries.

Location

This gateway to the Alaskan wilderness is a vibrant city of 290,000, and full of ambitious and adventurous young people who spend a lot of time working hard and enjoying outdoor recreational challenges.

UAA's 1700 acre main campus is located in an extensive greenbelt four miles southeast of downtown in the University-Medical District, adjacent to the Alaska Native Medical Center and Providence Alaska Medical Center. Campus facilities are connected by a network of paved, outdoor trails and an elevated indoor walkway that provides dry and warm access to major buildings.

Anchorage has a milder climate than other cities in Alaska, but winter still brings the snow and cold expected in this latitude, which is similar to Oslo, Norway.

Community

UAA's undergraduate community population of about 11,300 includes 91% Alaska residents, of which only 4800 are full time students. The out of state and international students who come to UAA are adventurous, want to experience a different physical and socio-cultural environment, and often have a particular interest in the distinct UAA programs that provide valuable industry connections.

There is a student-led **Life & Leadership** organization that cultivates an engaged campus community and offers students the opportunity to shape their own experience at UAA. It offers welcoming and inclusive events, involvement opportunities, leadership development, and ways to engage in purposeful service work.

The **UAA Diversity Action Council** awards scholarships to students who significantly enhance diversity at UAA, create a welcoming environment, and represent diverse student voices and cultures through advocacy and participation in UAA student organizations.

The impressive 5000 seat **Alaska Airlines Center** multi-purpose arena hosts athletic and large community events. AAU's 200 seat **Recital Hall** is a venue for concerts, lectures, plays, and other entertainment open to the community.

Academics

Arctic research, outdoor recreation courses, and a reputation for substantial and accessible undergraduate research opportunities bring students to UAA, as does its commitment to international and intercultural education and environmental concerns. The University has a 15:1 student-faculty ratio and is divided into five instructional and research units at the Anchorage campus.

It is important to note that the UA Higher Ed system is interconnected. Transfer from one UA campus to another is relatively easy, and UA maintains an enormous online education program to serve students in the many isolated Alaskan communities. The UA system previously suffered a budget crisis that impacted many departments but this challenge was met with committed, innovative thinking and is more robust than ever.

UAA's academic facilities include a planetarium located in the **ConocoPhillips Integrated Sciences Building**. This building also houses professional research-grade facilities and specialized labs. UAA offers unique opportunities to conduct field research in the Polar Regions because such complex ecosystems and extreme and changing environments surround the campus. The Civil Engineering program emphasizes northern-region design considerations. It provides specialized training appropriate for an engineering career in cold regions of the world and field research on coastal erosion, seismic performance of facilities, and problems with wind turbines on warming permafrost.

The Business Administration degree in **Global Logistics and Supply Chain Management** is especially relevant to critical problems in shipping and receiving goods that businesses are currently facing. As a strategic global center for international trade, Anchorage offers unique opportunities for professional internships and research.

The departments of Anthropology, Geography, and Environmental Studies, and the **Alaska Center for Conservation Science,** are housed together and share a wide variety of wet and dry labs for study and research. The **Environment and Natural Resource Institute** utilizes an **Ecosystem–Biomedical Health Laboratory**, which houses a specialized stable isotope lab.

The UAA College of Health offers strong nursing, health, and professional social work programs. The two adjacent medical centers provide training and internship sites.

Recreational Activities and Residential Life

The **Seawolf Sports Complex** supports a full range of sports events and facilities. The gym and other team facilities are used for intramural and club sports teams and varsity games. Varsity athletes compete in thirteen sports including women's gymnastics. At the 2022 Olympics, four former Seawolf athletes competed in skiing and hockey. **Outdoor Recreation** courses include ice climbing, sea kayaking, crevasse rescue technique, backcountry skiing, and winter camping.

The **Student Union** is headquarters for all recreational activities programs and over one hundred clubs and organizations. A **Multicultural Center,** two sororities, and three fraternities are active on campus. A radio station and newspaper are options for professional skills development.

The **First-Year Residential Experience Program** is a living/learning community housed in North Hall. FYRE helps residents with their transition to college. It provides peer support and mentoring, social events, workshops on academic success and personal growth, tutoring and study groups, and leadership and community service opportunities. Three residence halls offer suite style housing for 200 students, with most having private bedrooms and all having community kitchens and lounges. A six-building Main Apartment complex provides apartment style living for students who have lived on campus at least one year. UAA offers several meal plans.

Financial Aid

Honors College students get a housing scholarship. UAA is a **WUE** participant.

Study Away

UAA offers an **Education Abroad** program that gives opportunities for study, internships, or service learning in another country, while earning UAA credits. Students must have completed two full time semesters and have a 2.5 GPA to qualify.

Research Centers

The Alaska Center for Conservation Science (ACCS) is an excellent example of the campus Centers for research, education, and scholarship found on most large university campuses, especially those labeled as research universities.

These entities are committed to providing public, industry, and government agencies with critical information and accurate and current data through their primary and applied research. They are staffed by data managers and scientists and provide opportunities for student internships and research assistant positions on campus.

Campus-based Centers also collaborate with multiple partners, from government and state agencies to museums and non-profit organizations. The ACCS, for instance, maintains long- term datasets that are essential for providing the scientific basis for effective biological conservation in Alaska.

ACCS also works closely with community residents and agency partners on monitoring, education, training, conservation efforts, and stewardship of regional ecosystems.

University of Alaska Anchorage Basic Statistics

Undergraduate Enrollment	Freshman Class Enrollment	Institution Total FT, PT Enrollment	Female/Male Student Ratio	Female/Male Faculty Ratio	Student/ Faculty Ratio
10,342	990	10,895	60/40	56/44	10/1
# of 1st Year Applications	**# of 1st Year Women Admitted**	**# of 1st Year Men Admitted**	**# of Transfer Students Admitted**	**Overall Yield**	**% of Out-of-State Students**
3,431	1,375	994	1,058	42%	7%
% Students Living in Campus Housing	**Fraternity/ Sorority Participation**	**% Students Receiving Need-based Aid**	**1st Year Students Retention Rate**	**% Classes Under 30**	**% Caucasian/ White Faculty**
3.5%	n/a	51%	69%	97%	77%
# Caucasian / White Students	**# Hispanic / Latinx Students**	**# Asian Students**	**# Black Students**	**# American Indian/ Alaskan, Hawaiian /Native Pacific Islander**	**# International Students**
5,028	772	768	285	835	150
In-State Tuition and Fees	**Room and Board**	**Out-of-State Tuition and Fees**	**Honors Program Cost**	**Honors Program Grant**	**Athletic Division**
$7,014	$12,662	$21,142	n/a	varies	NCAA Div II

Notes:

University of Alaska Southeast

Juneau, Alaska / www.uas.alaska.edu

UAS offers a small college experience in a breathtakingly beautiful setting with a special attraction for students interested in an interdisciplinary perspective and hands-on research opportunities in the environmental sciences.

Location

Juneau is by far the most scenic state capital in the U.S. and one of the friendliest. A coastal city of 33,000, it sits at sea level at the base of steep and rugged mountains. Its abundant ocean and mountain wildlife and glacier viewing, as well as outdoor adventures, make it a prime tourist destination. The city is located within the **Tongass National Forest,** which provides an extraordinary natural laboratory, including marine habitat, rainforest, wetlands, and ice fields. Juneau can only be accessed by air or ferry.

The Juneau climate is milder than Anchorage's, but snowfall from November to March averages more than 86 inches, fall weather tends to be rainy, and spring is much dryer. The city has a small town feel but has plenty of pubs and restaurants and is rich in history, art, music, and Native Heritage.

An impressive 640 acre city-owned ski area is situated on an island just across the channel from the city. State government offices and tourism related businesses are the leading employers, and only 3% of the population has income below the poverty level.

Community

The main UAS campus, with residential housing, campus services, the library, and classrooms, is situated at beautiful Auke Bay. Career and technical education departments (CTE) are offered at a downtown campus. Students describe the campus community as tight-knit and supportive.

The **Student Activities Board, Student Engagement and Leadership Office,** and **Student Government** all share in the development and support of a lively on-campus learning community. These organizations play key roles in developing UAS community activities, addressing student interests and concerns, and designing student service programs.

The **Native and Rural Student Center** creates an inclusive student-centered community that honors diversity and celebrates cultural traditions and knowledge.

Academics

The Alaska higher education system is interconnected, and transfer from one campus to another is relatively easy. The UA system also has an enormous online education program to serve students in the many isolated Alaskan communities.

The UAS campus in Juneau specializes in interdisciplinary programs that give students a variety of tools and methodologies for dealing with complex problems and challenging issues. Student-faculty ratio is 10:1, and students commend the faculty for being passionate about their areas of expertise, promoting a positive atmosphere in UA's classes, and always being available. UAS classes are small and professors are rated as outstanding in their fields.

UAS's highly respected Biology and Marine Biology degrees are of interest for students wanting personalized and unique hands-on experience in a rich northern ocean environment and can include a fisheries science emphasis.

The **UAS Program on the Environment** structure allows students to explore widely before choosing an emphasis for a degree. B.S degrees in Environmental Resources and Environmental Science boast faculty whose research interests range from landscape ecology and hydrology to biogeochemistry and glaciology. There are ample opportunities for students to join in such research. The BA in Environmental Studies offers an emphasis on either environmental studies or outdoor studies.

In addition to exceptional environment-related academic programs, the University offers humanities, Native language and arts, natural sciences, social science, education, and business degrees that focus on learning through creative projects and research.

Because many faculty members are passionate researchers, students are encouraged to engage in research and creative activities inside and outside the classroom. Ambitious students can find paid work as lab and field research assistants for UAS faculty or even local agencies and organizations. The UAS **Alaska Coastal Rainforest Center,** for instance, is a Center focused on the impact of a warming climate on the environment and the challenges of the physical, economic, and cultural adaptations that all must make due to climate change.

Students can also obtain university funding to pursue research and creative project ideas that take advantage of the unique opportunities provided by the University's location.

Recreational Activities and Residential Living

Residential housing on the Juneau campus for first year students serves as a hub for social activities and academic services developed specifically to help new students succeed and acclimate. All housing residents are required to purchase a meal plan. There are apartment complexes for older students, gender-inclusive options, and students are placed in housing based on their gender identity.

Some merit-based housing scholarships provide cost reductions for students with good academic records. Campus dining options include the Lakeside Grill and Market and Spike's Café, a popular hangout for students and faculty.

The UAS **Recreation Center** has a full-court gym, climbing wall, suspended running track, cardio equipment, weight room, and studio. Intramural, club sports, and fitness training are offered. A year-round disc golf course is on the campus. From morning yoga on the dock to kayaking or world class backcountry skiing, UAS students make full use of the outdoor environment for both team and individual outdoor recreation at their chosen level of challenge.

Financial Aid

Out of state students from **WUE** states get tuition discounts. There are several different merit scholarships for both Alaskan and out of state students, and those with good GPA's can also get reductions on housing costs.

Study Away

Numerous study abroad programs are offered through the **Exchanges & Study Abroad Office.** UAS also participates in both the **International Student Exchange Program** and the **National Student Exchange.** The University of Oregon's **GEO** program is a popular choice for many because of its language immersion courses.

National Student Exchange

The idea of spending some time on another North American campus can be appealing for many reasons, and is a popular option at many colleges and universities.

Through the NSE exchange program a student majoring in marine science in Alaska, for example, might want to explore a marine environment in a different climate, or on a different coast. The student could choose the University of the Virgin Islands on St. Thomas, which happens to have a strong marine biology program, and credits earned there can be accepted at the student's home campus.

Applicants to NSE need to be carrying at least a 2.5 GPA, have a clean record, and some good recommendations. Applying early will increase the chance of getting one of the limited spots available.

If accepted for an NSE exchange, the student will gain a different perspective on their field of study, experience valuable cultural immersion, and come back to the home campus with greater self-confidence, a wider knowledge of their field, and a nice addition to their resume.

University of Alaska Southeast Basic Statistics

Undergraduate Enrollment	Freshman Class Enrollment	Institution Total FT, PT Enrollment	Female/Male Student Ratio	Female/Male Faculty Ratio	Student/ Faculty Ratio
1,757	149	1,997	66/34	56/44	8/1
# of 1st Year Applications	**# of 1st Year Women Admitted**	**# of 1st Year Men Admitted**	**# of Transfer Students Admitted**	**Overall Yield**	**% of Out-of-State Students**
464	164	97	215	57%	12%
% Students Living in Campus Housing	**Fraternity/ Sorority Participation**	**% Students Receiving Need-based Aid**	**1st Year Students Retention Rate**	**% Classes Under 30**	**% Caucasian/ White Faculty**
10%	n/a	50%	65%	99.4%	88%
# Caucasian / White Students	**# Hispanic / Latinx Students**	**# Asian Students**	**# Black Students**	**# American Indian/ Alaskan, Hawaiian /Native Pacific Islander**	**# International Students**
958	116	57	15	276	19
In-State Tuition and Fees	**Room and Board**	**Out-of-State Tuition and Fees**	**Honors Program Cost**	**Honors Program Grant**	**Athletic Division**
$7,000	$10,200	$21,096	n/a	n/a	n/a

Notes:

Boise State University

Boise, Idaho / www.boisestate.edu

Boise State has made a solid commitment to innovation and offers plenty of undergraduate research, sports, arts, and outdoor recreation options in a fast growing metro area that is a thriving Pacific Northwest center for technology research and marketing.

Location

Boise is the third-largest city in the Pacific Northwest and the Idaho state capital. The total metro area population is close to 750,000 and is attracting a substantial inflow of new residents moving from other states. Numerous tech companies, such as Micron, software startups, energy and manufacturing companies, and state government offices provide employment and internship opportunities.

Situated on the Boise River, the city is noted for the Boise Greenbelt. This runs 25 miles through the city and along the river. Boise boasts 89 city parks as well. The population is 89% white, although this includes a large ethnic Basque community that adds cultural diversity. Downtown Boise has plenty of entertainment venues, restaurants, bars and clubs, theaters, and shopping districts to explore and enjoy.

The climate is semi-arid with four distinct seasons, including hot summers, but not much snow in winter.

Community

At Boise State, the **Student Involvement and Leadership Center** serves as the hub for information and programming that supports a sense of community and sponsors or promotes events and conversations.

Programs such as **Courageous Dialogues** and a six-day **LeaderShape** experience explore the roles of perception and influence in creating a just, caring, and thriving world.

Greek life plays a role in community life on the University campus. Twenty-three small and large chapters are active in providing social fun, service, and fostering academic achievement and leadership.

As in many larger institutions, students here develop their social communities around their particular intellectual interests, passions, identities, and needs.

Boise State is aware of a need to unite the faculty and staff in fostering a more diverse, inclusive, and equitable campus environment and is actively training employees through their innovative **BUILD** program.

Academics

The most popular departments here are nursing and psychology, followed by biology, computer science, health studies, and kinesiology. With a student to faculty ratio of 18:1, BSU students report that the workload is generally manageable, the instructors by and large helpful, and the professors who teach in the **Honors Program** are exceptional.

BSU prides itself on its culture of innovation in research and has structured programs to transcend disciplines. This culture encourages collaboration among people from different academic and technology fields. The **College of Innovation and Design** is an incubator for ideas that will enable the University to anticipate emerging trends and meet current and future workforce needs. It is also a resource and support for student entrepreneurs, integrated projects, and environmental challenges. A **Maker Lab** in the library provides coaches for entrepreneurial ideas and product development and has accessible technology and a multimedia studio.

There are also numerous research centers and institutes active on the campus, such as the **Center for Orthopedic and Biomechanics Research,** which is a partnership between the departments of Kinesiology and Mechanical and Biomedical Engineering.

The **Institute for Inclusive and Transformative Scholarship** supports undergraduate research and grants. Students usually work in research teams and are assigned lab and field work that assists in solving the problems and building the data needed to achieve a research project's goals. The **Career Services** office places hundreds of students each year with local and regional organizations to gain on the ground experience and build their resumes and skill sets through internships.

A new **Center for the Visual Arts** brings multiple programs together under one roof with state of the art studios and equipment. The music and theater departments also have strong support and participation at Boise.

Recreational Activities and Residential Life

The University website lists many clubs and professional organizations, including the BAJA Racing Club, a Food Recovery Network, the Gender Equity Center, the Jedi Academy, a Maker Club, sports clubs, and varied ethnic community associations.

Twenty-five club sports are student-run. Most clubs have non-player coaches and compete in local, regional, and even national competitions. These include water polo, lacrosse, boxing, and rodeo. An **Outdoor Program** is available, and climbing, hiking, kayaking, and trips to nearby ski areas are favorites. Intramural Sports are also popular for both recreational and competitive athletes. BSU varsity athletes compete at NCAA Division I level in the Mountain West Conference. Varsity teams include six sports for men and ten for women.

The University offers residential housing for first year students in nine different halls with various room and suite designs. Additional residences serve older students. A weekly meal plan is required for first year students. The Honors students have special housing in a centrally located five story hall. Living/learning communities are available for students with shared interests, such as the Health Professions or STEM Education.

There is no heavy party scene on campus since fraternity and sorority houses are located off campus, but downtown bars, late night coffee shops, and various entertainment options are just a few blocks away in the busy downtown area.

Financial Aid

Most students receive some level of financial aid, and both in state and out of state students can apply for the larger **Treasure Scholarship.** Boise State is a **WUE** participant. There are some athletic scholarships offered as well.

Study Away

BSU's **Global Opportunities** program links students to study away opportunities, including the **National Student Exchange.** A **Global Classrooms** program encourages students to join short-term faculty-led programs related to a course, and there are international internship opportunities as well.

Maker Labs

Maker Labs, or **Maker Spaces**, are a relatively new campus amenity. They are multiplying because equipment costs have shrunk as demand by a new generation of tech-savvy college students has increased.

Although hands-on experimentation is hardly a new concept for engineering or art departments, these new maker spaces are intended to draw in students from all disciplines and encourage cross-disciplinary, innovative thinking.

The 21st century demands a workforce with critical thinking and problem solving skills. These maker spaces are designed to meet that demand by encouraging and supporting competency and experience in collaborative project development, technology skills, creative communication, and the entrepreneurial mindset that today's employers are seeking. Finding adequate space to house a maker lab is a struggle for many campuses, and sometimes these maker labs are crammed into small spaces, often in libraries, sometimes in residential halls.

Some of the most impressive maker spaces include a comfortable lounge in which to brainstorm ideas with others, a room with 3D printers, laser cutters, and electronics workstations, and workshops for fabrication, woodworking, sewing, and metalwork. The best examples are intentionally designed as part of new campus building construction or a renovation project, and planned with substantial input from students and faculty.

Boise State University Basic Statistics

Undergraduate Enrollment	Freshman Class Enrollment	Institution Total Enrollment	Female/Male Student Ratio	Female/Male Faculty Ratio	Student/ Faculty Ratio
22,433	3,195	25,830	57/43	55/45	18/1
# of 1st Year Applications	**# of 1st Year Women Admitted**	**# of 1st Year Men Admitted**	**# of Transfer Students Admitted**	**Overall Yield**	**% of Out-of-State Students**
15,648	7,670	5,338	2,745	20%	43%
% Students Living in Campus Housing	**Fraternity/ Sorority Participation**	**% Students Receiving Need-based Aid**	**1st Year Students Retention Rate**	**% Classes Under 30**	**% Caucasian/ White Faculty**
63% of freshmen	10%	48%	76%	67%	88%
# Caucasian / White Students	**# Hispanic / Latinx Students**	**# Asian Students**	**# Black Students**	**# American Indian/ Alaskan, Hawaiian /Native Pacific Islander**	**# International Students**
16,210	3,088	603	325	185	162
In-State Tuition and Fees	**Room and Board**	**Out-of-State Tuition and Fees**	**Honors Program Cost**	**Honors Program Grant**	**Athletic Division**
$8,364	$11,000	$25,701	$100 per semester	varies	NCAA Div. I

Notes:

University of British Columbia-Okanagan

Kelowna, B.C. / www. ok.ubc.ca

The University of British Columbia's stunning eastern campus is new enough to be both state of the art in its facilities and fiercely innovative in its philosophy of learning and teaching.

Location

The city of Kelowna is located on the eastern shore of the spectacular 84 mile long Okanagan Lake in southern British Columbia. This fast growing metro area has beaches, access to a long-distance rail trail for bikers and hikers, and is surrounded by regional and provincial parks.

Okanagan Lake and Kelowna City. B.C.

The four season climate has a warm summer, a three-month cold season with an average high in the low 40's, and over 300 sunny days a year.

Considered the number one entrepreneurial region of Canada, the **Okanagan Centre for Innovation** is a hub of technology, entrepreneurship, and creativity. The city has 663 tech businesses and counting. Kelowna has a lively downtown and waterfront area offering all the amenities of a large and thriving city. The Kelowna International airport is served by multiple airlines.

Community

This UBCO campus serves 8109 full time undergraduates. About 23% are students from other countries. The campus offers a close-knit and connected environment for learning and research.

The **Equity and Inclusion Office** leads action and dialogue to build a campus community "in which human rights are respected, and equity and inclusion are embedded in all areas of academic, work, and campus life."

The University's **Intercultural Development Program** builds cross cultural and communication skills and understanding, and special support services are available for its large population of international students.

The campus hosts upwards of 2500 campus events each year, including workshops, speakers, symposiums, concerts and social events.

Academics

Canadian universities refer to Faculties instead of Departments, and UBCO offers eight Faculties that serve undergraduates. Most bachelor programs can be combined with a salaried **CO-OP Work Experience** placement taken in the third year for 4, 8, or even 12 months.

A **Creative and Critical Studies** program offers humanities and language studies, media, visual and performing arts, cultural studies, creative writing and literature.

Engineering students benefit from an interdisciplinary and project–based approach to learning and can specialize in civil, electrical, or mechanical engineering. Health and Exercise Sciences, Nursing, and Social Work programs are housed in the **Faculty of Health and Social Development.** This faculty also transcends disciplines with its strong collaborative research emphasis on health challenges.

Psychology, History, Sociology, Philosophy, Political Science, and a Community, Culture and Global Studies program are in the **Arts and Social Sciences** Faculty, which focuses on economic, social, and cultural change. The Faculties of **Education** and of **Management** are equally innovative and collaborative in their approach to learning. Students report that the **Faculty of Science** professors are accessible and foster team-based research and interconnectedness among the sciences and technology. Uncommon science specialties offered are Ecology and Evolutionary Biology, Medical Physics, and Freshwater Science.

Recreational Activities and Residential Living

The **Student Union** connects incoming students with student clubs and associations and manages the full calendar of campus happenings. The **Student Union Pub** is one of several gathering places in the large and ultramodern **University Center** that also houses a sushi restaurant, coffee house, and café. The Centre itself is the hub of student activity and engagement.

The **Pritchard Dining Hall** is an all you can eat dining experience open from 7am to 9:30 pm daily. It offers a Plantopia station featuring locally sourced vegetables and grains and where all ingredients are plant sourced, and many other stations with a wide variety of meal options. Other cafes, pubs, and a coffeehouse are scattered around the campus. There are nine residence areas on campus and first year students live in residences with single rooms. Older students have access to suite-style residences. Well-trained Residence Life Teams encourage fun gatherings and events and connections to student services. Living/ Learning Communities are paired with a faculty member who serves as advisor and develops extra-curricular programs and educational opportunities.

For skiers and snowboarders the **Big White Ski Resort,** just 35 miles away, hosts World Cup events. Students can get involved in intramurals, club sports, fitness classes and various outdoor recreation courses and trips. Varsity athletes compete in six sports in the Canada West conference and UBCO has an emphasis on recruiting scholar-athletes. There is a new LEED certified **Aquatic Centre** that harvests rain water for its 50M Competition Pool and 25M recreation pool, plus a Leisure Pool, hot tub, steam room, and sauna.

Financial Aid

UBCO students from the U.S. can use the U.S. Federal Education Loans, but not Pell grants. Canadian students have a range of financial aid opportunities. U.S. and other International Students can be awarded merit, community service, and extracurricular-based scholarships and can also do work study and access paid co-op opportunities.

Study Away

Go Global programs at UBCO include exchange programs and a wide variety of other study abroad options. **Global Seminars** are offered by UBCO faculty members and will earn credits. Indonesia, Iceland, Greece, Poland, China, and the European Union are trips offered recently as Global Seminars.

Cooperative Education Work Experiences

The value of gaining work experience in your field of interest while in college is very clear. Both internships and co-op programs offer such opportunities. Typically a co-op is a paid, full-time work experience for which **students also receive some college credit**. They are offered as part of the curriculum of a specific academic department that partners with a company or organization to offer the cooperative education experience.

One advantage of a co-op job is that having time off from college can make a four year degree more affordable. Many co-ops pay well and the FAFSA does not consider income from student co-op jobs when determining your eligibility for financial aid. On the other hand it may take longer to get that degree, depending on the number of credits the co-op experience offers.

The differences between internships and co-op programs have become less distinct over the years, with some internships being paid and even required in some degree programs.

What has not changed is the immense real world value to the college student of having responsible work experiences and employer references on their resumes, especially those directly relevant to their career objectives.

University of British Columbia-Okanagan Basic Statistics

Undergraduate Enrollment	Freshman Class Enrollment	Institution Total Enrollment	Female/Male Student Ratio	Female/Male Faculty Ratio	Student/ Faculty Ratio
8,109	2,475	11,989	53/47	--	23/1
# of 1st Year Applications	**# of 1st Year Women Admitted**	**# of 1st Year Men Admitted**	**# of Transfer Students Admitted**	**Overall Yield**	**% of Out of Canada Students**
--	--	--	--	49%	22%
% Students Living on Campus	**Fraternity/ Sorority Participation**	**% Students Receiving Need-based Financial Aid**	**1st Year Students Retention Rate**	**% of Classes Under 30**	**% Caucasian/ White Faculty**
18%	n/a	--	89%	33%	--
%Caucasian / White Students	**% Hispanic / Latinx Students**	**% Asian Students**	**% Black Students**	**% American Indian/ Alaskan, Hawaiian /Native Pacific Islander**	**% Inter-national Students**
--	--	--	--	6.3%	22%
In-Country Tuition and Fees	**Room and Board**	**International Tuition and Fees**	**Honors Program Cost**	**Honors Program Scholarshop**	**Athletic Division**
$6,563 CAD$	$10,859 CAD$	$46,637 CAD$	n/a	n/a	Canada West

Notes:

Central Washington University

Ellensburg, Washington / www.cwu.edu

This midsized state university is known for its diversity, innovative curriculum, and deep commitment to supporting students in their transition to college, and along their career pathways.

Location

Ellensburg is a historic college town located in the foothills just east of the Cascades Mountain Range and along the Yakima River in a rich agricultural region. The area enjoys a semi-arid climate with little snow and relatively mild winters, but warm summers.

Ellensburg residents are active outdoors, use the extended trail system for hiking and biking, the nearby ski areas for winter sports, and access miles of cross country and snowmobiling territory. There is premier fly fishing in the 27 mile long Yakima River Canyon, which is also popular for rafting and camping.

Ellensburg boasts an award-winning downtown, an eclectic food scene, and great breweries. The University is the largest employer in a population of 21,600. The city has a riverfront park and numerous trails, including the 250 mile Cascades State Park Rail Trail that passes through the city on its way to the Columbia River.

Community

CWU has earned prestigious awards for its commitment to diversity and inclusion. This friendly 380 acre campus provides good opportunities and resources even for students who come less prepared than others. About 7% of its undergrads come to CWU from out of state. Students of color are well represented at CWU. A **Heritage Spanish** program helps heritage Spanish speakers raise their written and communication skills to a professional level.

The student experience at CWU begins with **Orientation** and the **University 101** course all students must take in their first quarter of study. UNIV 101 is designed to foster a successful transition, encourage participation in curricular and extracurricular activities, and inform students about services and resources. Among these resources are identity-based and cultural programs, and clubs that help students affirm their self-identity and lived experiences.

CWU focuses on developing a sense of belonging and connection to place and a sense of ownership that leads to empowerment and shared governance. The **Diversity and Equity Center** provides holistic support and programs to cultivate this sense of belonging. An **InterClub Association** supports student clubs and provides funding for club projects, leadership training, and activities.

Academics

Students report that professors are engaging, caring, and accessible, and the work load manageable. Although there are some large lecture classes, most classes are under thirty students. CWU has a strong reputation as an excellent school of education, and over twenty percent of students major in an education-related field. Business and marketing also attracts many students, as do the social sciences, psychology, and computer sciences. CWU's College of Business teams have a stellar record of winning the **Boeing Northwest Case Competition** and CWU maintains a strong relationship with the Boeing Company

An interesting interdisciplinary degree in Business and Marketing Teacher Preparation is offered and responds to a severe shortage of teachers in that field. There are solid programs in law enforcement and firefighting and other protective services. CWU also offers a top program in Aviation Education, offering B.S degrees for flight officers and commercial pilots as well as aviation management degrees.

The department of Engineering Technology, Safety, and Construction offers B.S degrees in ten different specialties and is taught in the **Hogue Technology Addition**, a nationally recognized model of Leadership in Energy and Environmental Design. The Physics Department also has a new building with a planetarium and observatory and a variety of lab spaces. It has award-winning faculty who excel in teaching as well as research.

CWU's **Geodesy Laboratory** processes data from the **Pacific Northwest Geodetic Array** of receivers monitoring tectonics, earthquake, and tsunami events; an exciting opportunity for undergraduates interested in geological sciences and related research.

The Music department is a leader in K-12 Music Education and wind band instruction and the **CWU Marching Band** is nationally renowned.

Recreational Activities and Residential Life

There are numerous student clubs and organizations on campus, from sports clubs, to equity and service organizations, to professional career-related groups. Several programs are focused on building community and connections including a well-funded **Center for Leadership and Engagement**, **Student Government**, and the **Student Involvement Office.** The CWU **Student Union** serves as a hub for activities and events.

About a third of students participate in Intramural Sports. The **Outdoor Pursuits and Rentals** program offers trips, including bus transport to nearby ski areas, equipment rentals, and special events like 'full moon night' cross-country skiing and adventure movie screenings. **Wildcat Farm** grows fresh produce for the CWU Dining Services, offers volunteer and project opportunities for students, and serves as an outdoor classroom for some courses.

CWU requires first year students to live on campus unless they live locally. Students can choose academic Living/Learning Communities based on common majors or in theme houses. Both have informal and formal activities and connections with faculty to enhance their educational experiences and build a sense of "home away from home." CWU varsity athletes compete at Division II level in the Northwest Athletic Conference in six men's sports, including rugby, and seven women's sports, including rugby and soccer.

Financial Aid

WUE students pay 150% of in state tuition and some students from certain counties in Idaho and Oregon only pay in-state tuition and fees. There are performance and talent awards offered in Athletics, Music, and Theater Arts. The **Honors College** offers scholarships and partial tuition waivers to highly qualified students accepted into this innovative interdisciplinary program.

Study Away

The **Office of International Studies and Programs** offers multiple opportunities and some financial aid for education abroad. Students can Minor in **International Studies** and participate in the CWU **International House** activities. CWU also has a program with Tokyo Gakugei University.

Heritage Spanish Programs

Heritage Spanish programs are becoming popular on many campuses, especially at colleges and universities with high numbers of Spanish heritage speakers. A student who was raised in a home in which Spanish is the primary language spoken, but who has learned English during their elementary and high school years, is termed a Heritage Spanish language speaker.

College students with this background often still speak, or at least understand, the heritage language, or some form of Spanglish, and thus are, to some degree, bi-lingual but may not be proficient enough to read, write, and communicate professionally in the heritage language.

In addition to enhancing their connection to their cultural heritage and communities, Heritage Spanish programs seek to improve the student's literacy and oral skills and encourage bilingualism and biliteracy.

The curricula of these courses differ from regular Spanish language classes designed for students who have had no home exposure to the language. The diversity of the Spanish language is accepted, and instructors do not impose their own variety of Spanish as the only correct one. There is also an emphasis on ensuring that these students have a sense of worth and validation for their bicultural perspectives and bilingual competencies.

Central Washington University Basic Statistics

Undergraduate Enrollment	Freshman Class Enrollment	Institution Total Enrollment	Female/Male Student Ratio	Female/Male Faculty Ratio	Student/ Faculty Ratio
10,317	1,891	11,213	54/46	53/47	24/1
# of 1st Year Applications	**# of 1st Year Women Admitted**	**# of 1st Year Men Admitted**	**# of Transfer Students Admitted**	**Overall Yield**	**% of Out-of-State Students**
10,408	6,265	4,163	1,967	15%	7%
% Students Living in Campus After 1st Year	**Fraternity/ Sorority Participation**	**% Students Receiving Need-based Aid**	**1st Year Students Retention Rate**	**% Classes Under 30**	**% Caucasian/ White Faculty**
15%	0	63%	70%	74%	86%
# Caucasian / White Students	**# Hispanic / Latinx Students**	**# Asian Students**	**# Black Students**	**# American Indian/ Alaskan, Hawaiian /Native Pacific Islander**	**# International Students**
5,338	1,868	502	452	101	269
In-State Tuition and Fees	**Room and Board Average**	**Out-of-State Tuition and Fees**	**Honors Program Cost**	**Honors Program Scholarship**	**Athletic Division**
$8,885	$13,787	$25,909	0	$1000 per year	Div II

Notes:

In Focus: Uncommon Majors

Major	Description
AQUARIUM SCIENCE **Western Oregon University**	An innovative and collaborative B.S. in Aquarium Science, in which scuba diving becomes one of your many expert skills.
ANTHROZOOLOGY **Carroll College**	Interdisciplinary study of human interaction with other species, and how to improve these relationships. Relates to careers in veterinary medicine, animal assisted therapies, wildlife conservation, animal training, and humane education.
ASTROBIOLOGY **University of Washington**	The study of life in the universe that develops an understanding of life and the nature of the environments that support it, as well as planetary system, and stellar interactions and processes.
CLIMATE AND ENVIRONMENTAL JUSTICE **Evergreen State College**	Involves study of the relationship between human impacts on the Earth, its climate, and social inequalities among human communities in order to identify just and equitable solutions to the climate crisis.
CRAFT BREWING **Central Washington University**	An interdisciplinary, hands-on B.S. degree combining several sciences, sensory evaluation, engineering, business, merchandising elements, and internships with businesses focused on the craft of brewing.
ENERGY SYSTEMS ENGINEERING **Oregon State U-Cascades**	One of only six in the nation, this multidisciplinary major offers engineering fundamentals with energy-focused technical and business management courses that explore all types of energy.
FIRST NATIONS STUDIES **University of Montana**	Studies of indigenous political theory and politics, aesthetics, literature, and contemporary social concerns. Combines critical scholarship with ethical community engagement and a research practicum.
FISHERIES **University of Alaska (UAF)**	A program for studying and managing living marine resources and habitats. Offers research and internship options and Fisheries Business, Social Science or Rural and Community Development concentrations.

Major	Description
FOLKLORE AND PUBLIC CULTURE University of Oregon	Explores cultural practices and expressions, traditional knowledge, lore, and meaning, their history and how they become sources of identity, continuity, and meaning. Focuses on experiential fieldwork.
GAMES, INTERACTIVE MEDIA, AND MOBILE STUDIES Boise State University	Explores all elements of game design, creation, production, and deployment, such as visual, audio, storytelling, and virtual reality. Includes programming, coding logic, collaborative and project development management, iterative processes and prototyping, and user research.
JUDAIC STUDIES College of Idaho	Studies traditions of the Jewish people, how Judaism relates to and interacts with other religions and cultures, and offers study tours to Europe/Israel/Palestine.
OUTDOOR PRODUCTS Oregon State University-Cascades Campus	Prepares students for jobs in all aspects of the outdoor products industry. Emphasizes innovative thinking, development of skills and knowledge to meet the future needs of the industry, and internships with local industry.
SCIENTIFIC GLASSBLOWING Montana Western University	The art of producing and repairing scientific glass containers and apparatuses suitable for scientific research and complex products requires technical precision and proficiency. Art majors can also get a technical foundation in the principles of torch worked glass.
SUSTAINABLE RURAL SYSTEMS AND CONSERVATION Eastern Oregon University and Skagit Valley College	Offers group based learning, hands-on community engagement, and field work. Addresses agricultural environmental contamination, remediation, rural economic development, and policy. Encourages leadership in water quality issues and nearshore environments.
VITICULTURE AND ENOLOGY AND BUSINESS OF WINE Washington State U. and Linfield University	Programs that focus on grape growing, winemaking, and the business of wine. Contributes to critical research that strengthens the wine industry. Provides the technical, scientific, and practical experience needed to produce and market high quality grapes and premium wines.

**similar and related programs may be offered at other PNW institutions.*

Cal Poly Humboldt

Arcata, California / www.Humboldt.edu

Newly designated as a California Polytechnic University, Humboldt is adding 12 new STEM programs by 2023 and expects an increase in enrollment and greater campus resources from the state. Its combination of liberal arts and creative and experiential interdisciplinary curriculum serves a diverse student population.

Location

Arcata is a progressive college town situated on the upper northwest coast of the state and known for environmental protection and social justice activism. The award winning **Arcata Marsh**, a constructed network of salt water and fresh water ponds, provides an environmentally healthy wastewater treatment system. Its 2100 acres of city-owned and conserved **Redwood Forest** supports outstanding wildlife habitats and offers miles of hiking and biking trails and nature study opportunities.

In the heart of the small city's historic downtown is a large Plaza that hosts everything from a Saturday Farmers Market to an Oyster Festival to a Kinetic Sculpture Race and a Migrant Bird Festival. The streets surrounding the Plaza are lively with restaurants, pubs, coffeehouses, and an eclectic range of shops. Climate is typical coastal weather with warm dry summers, average temperatures in the mid to high 60s, and variable cloud cover.

Community

Students attest to the inclusive, welcoming sense of community at Humboldt. Its small size, compared to most California State institutions, and its close connection with the town and region, are attractive features. Humboldt students are described as friendly and polite. The University is nationally recognized as both a **Hispanic Serving Institution** and a **Minority Serving** one.

Career and Volunteer Expos bring businesses and community organizations to campus to facilitate these community-campus connections. Humboldt has expanded their **Immigration Legal Services** for students and faculty and partners with the Coalition for Humane Immigrant Rights.

El Centro Académico Cultural is committed to student success with a responsive approach, which includes the development of academic, intellectual, personal, and professional growth. El Centro is one of five **Cultural Centers of Academic Excellence** at HSU, including the **Indian Tribal & Educational Personnel Program (ITEPP),** the **Social Justice Equity & Inclusion Center** and the **Umoja Center for Pan African Student Excellence.**

Academics

In addition to providing a road map for academic pursuits early on, Humboldt works hard at getting students career-related opportunities for volunteer work and internships as they develop their knowledge and skills.

The natural environment-related STEM fields are exceptionally strong at Humboldt and opportunities for field research and hands-on experience are abundant. The most popular majors are based in the College of Natural Resources and Sciences, while the College of Arts, Humanities, and Social Sciences, and the College of Professional Studies are not far behind, making for a good balance of different student interests.

The University has more than three hundred courses with a sustainability theme. There are numerous institutes at Humboldt that engage students in research, including an **Interdisciplinary Marijuana Research Institute** and ones for **Cartographic Design, Rural Policy, Biological Anthropology, Altruistic Personality** and **Prosocial Behavior.** The **Campus Center for Appropriate Technology** is a demonstration home that began, and continues, as a student project to show how homes and grounds can be sustainably efficient and eco-crafted.

The **Schatz Energy Research Center** provides opportunities for students to engage in applied research on clean and renewable energy technologies such as offshore wind energy. The University owns a large ocean-going research vessel and has the **Telonicher Marine Lab,** both of which serve as outdoor classrooms and wet labs for hands-on study in everything from oceanography to beginning scuba.

Encouraging creativity and open minded exploration are major goals of all of Humboldt's academic programs. The film program in the Department of Theater, Film, and Dance has a mission to train students as an "independent voice," along with developing the tools for a professional career. The **Department of Critical Race, Gender, and Sexuality Studies** intersects ethnic, women's and multicultural queer studies and includes hands-on organizing practice in the community. Business students have the option of concentrating in **New Venture Management** after completing their foundation courses.

Recreational Activities and Residential Life

Humboldt has three first year student residence halls, two of which are traditional rooms with communal bathrooms and one with suite style living, while older students have apartment style housing. Many students move off campus into group houses in Arcata after the first year and meal plans are available to them. Passes for town buses are free.

Intramural and competitive club sports are active on campus and at the well-equipped student recreation center. The **Outdoor Recreation and Adventure** program supplies boat and kayak rental and instruction, outdoor equipment, guided trips, and certifications. Varsity athletes compete in four men's and seven women's sports at NCAA Division II level.

There are 170 clubs and organizations that students can get involved in including professional ones such as the American Indian Science and Engineering Society, cultural arts ones like Ballet Folklorico de Humboldt, and others such as an E Sports League club. A low key version of Greek life has a presence on campus.

Financial Aid

Students who come from **WUE** states can take advantage of the WUE tuition discount. Humboldt offers a large number of scholarships, some of which are renewable. Low income First Generation students can apply for an **Educational Opportunity Program**.

Study Away

A **Global Ambassadors Fund** supports students planning to study abroad and some language majors are actually required to do so. Faculty-led study abroad summer programs and bilateral exchanges are available as well.

Interdisciplinary Marijuana Research Institute

Given that the marijuana industry in northern California has had a significant impact on the region's economy and reputation since the 1960's, it is not surprising that this Institute, formed in 2012 as the first academic research organization devoted to marijuana, has received substantial grant funding.

California legalized medical marijuana in 1996 and recreational use in 2016. With a research and policy analysis mission, the Institute serves as both an informational clearing house and a collaborative center, and as a supporter of original research and scholarly scientific study of marijuana related issues. It does not advocate for or take a position on legalization or decriminalization of cannabis.

The Institute's challenges are in collecting data for valid assessment of the cannabis industry on the region's economy, physical and social well-being, energy consumption, land use, water quality and resources, health and human services, and police, fire, and emergency services.

Over the next two years, Cal Poly Humboldt intends to launch nine or ten new programs that draw on its STEM, environmental and social responsibility, and experiential learning strengths. An interdisciplinary Bachelor of Art in Cannabis Studies is one of these proposed new programs, along with a considerable expansion of Humboldt's engineering degree options, and a B.S. in Geospatial Information Science and Technology.

Cal Poly Humboldt Basic Statistics

Undergraduate Enrollment	Freshman Class Enrollment	Institution Total Enrollment	Female/Male Student Ratio	Female/Male Faculty Ratio	Student/ Faculty Ratio
5,201	629	5,739	59/41	57/43	18/1
# of 1st Year Applications	**# of 1st Year Women Admitted**	**# of 1st Year Men Admitted**	**# of Transfer Students Admitted**	**Overall Yield**	**% of Out-of-State Students**
7,025	3,920	2,478	3,111	10%	7%
% Students Living in Campus After 1st Year	**% Fraternity/ Sorority Participation**	**% Students Receiving Need-based Aid**	**1st Year Students Retention Rate**	**% Classes Under 30**	**% Caucasian/ White Faculty**
27%	1%	53%	73.70%	74%	71%
# Caucasian / White Students	**# Hispanic / Latinx Students**	**# Asian Students**	**# Black Students**	**# American Indian/ Alaskan, Hawaiian /Native Pacific Islander**	**# International Students**
2,627	1,287	176	222	37	60
In-State Tuition and Fees	**Room and Board Average**	**Out-of-State Tuition and Fees**	**Honors Program Cost**	**Honors Program Scholarship**	**Athletic Division**
$7,858	$12,540	$19,738	0	0	NCAA II

Notes:

Evergreen State College

Olympia, Washington / www.evergreen.edu

Evergreen's innovative open curriculum supports individualistic and self-motivated student explorers who want the freedom and flexibility to self-design their unique course of study.

Location

Evergreen's lush and heavily forested one thousand acre campus is located on a peninsula seven miles west of the lively port city of Olympia, the state capital, and at the southernmost tip of Puget Sound. The climate is relatively mild in all seasons, but being a coastal environment, it can also be humid and cloudy.

Olympia offers an historic downtown, three waterfront parks, and numerous state office buildings. The city is a regional hub for local arts and culture and has a designated **Creative District**, which utilizes transformed former warehouses and industrial structures as maker and performance spaces. The popular and growing Olympia metro area includes many smaller townships and has a total population of nearly 300,000, in which twenty-three percent identify as other than white.

Community

The Evergreen community is very progressive and student-driven and known for supporting and encouraging individualism, exploration, and involvement. The staff and faculty are friendly and helpful, and diversity and acceptance are a common theme.

The **Evergreen Student Civic Engagement Institute** is a six-day program for newly admitted undergraduates that introduces diverse students to Evergreen's community resources and mission and helps them acclimate to the unique academic structure.

The **Center for Community-based Learning and Action** provides hands-on opportunities for faculty and students to work collaboratively with area organizations on a range of critical community issues, with the goal of putting theory into action.

Faculty members often host potlucks at their homes, and a small lodge on the campus farm is a popular place to hold retreats. The **Longhouse Education and Cultural Center,** the **First Peoples Multicultural, Trans, and Queer Support Services,** and the **Inclusive Excellence and Success** programs provide resources for and support of diversity and equity at Evergreen.

Academics

The appeal for many who enroll at Evergreen is the DIY freedom it offers. You can choose how to mix a variety of your interests, select whichever courses seem relevant, and then settle on an area of emphasis within a Field of Study.

The majority of classes at Evergreen have fewer than 30 students. The student to faculty ratio is 16:1 and 24% of faculty members are members of minority groups. There are more than forty Fields of Study to choose from and most are interdisciplinary and innovative in blending traditional disciplines into an interconnected whole and then encouraging students to apply this interconnected understanding to complex problems. One drawback is that transferring these inventive courses' credits to a more traditional university can be problematic.

There are no specific prerequisites or specific courses required for a B.A. degree, just a minimum number of credits. For a B.S. degree in Science, a certain number of credits must be earned in science, math, or computer science, and a certain number must be in upper level coursework. Additional credits are required for the combined BS degree in Arts and Science.

For students who are more comfortable with a **Preplanned Pathway,** there are eleven guided programs of interdisciplinary studies such as Political Economy, Global Studies and Environmental Justice, or Psychology, Health and Community. For either the free choice or preplanned option, courses are ranked as Entry, Intermediate, or Advanced level to plan a pathway that builds on prior knowledge and skills and provides checkpoints on progress toward a degree. There are no grades at Evergreen, only **Narrative Evaluations** by both instructor(s) and student which provide examples of academic progress, credits earned, and comments on attendance, class preparation, and teamwork.

The highly flexible DIY academic structure does not work for everyone. Some students can get lost in the plethora of intriguing choices and find themselves off course for graduation or career preparation. However, most Evergreen students comment that this system of performance rating lends itself to healthy levels of self-reflection and accountability for one's own education. Evergreen students also appreciate the emphasis on hands-on work.

Recreational Activities and Residential Life

Students can enjoy an extensive network of trails in the forest, Puget Sound beaches, and an **Organic Farm** right on campus, not to mention the outdoor recreation opportunities of the surrounding region with its state and national forests, mountains, and Pacific coast.

Evergreen campus housing is all furnished apartment-style with four to six private bedrooms, shared bathrooms and open space living and kitchen areas in newly remodeled residences. A central building serves as a community hub with laundry, mailroom, a market, and more. Meals are nutritious and a meal plan is required for residents.

The **Constanito Recreation Center** offers cardio and weight rooms, a climbing gym, racquetball courts, and the main gymnasium and dance studio. A pool and sauna complex also includes dance and yoga spaces. Varsity sports include basketball, soccer, and outdoor track and field for men and women, plus volleyball for women, with teams competing with other small colleges in the NAIA, and in the Cascade Collegiate Conference. Competitive Club Sports include Baseball, Crew, Wrestling, and Softball.

Student clubs and organizations range from one focusing on Japanese animation to **WashPIRG**, a student public interest activism group promoting civic engagement and building leadership skills through internships. Students also manage the **Cooper Point Journal**, a campus newspaper that reflects student concerns and contributions and serves as a learning laboratory in organizational collaboration and shared responsibility for staff volunteers.

Financial Aid

Evergreen students from Washington have access to a need-based grant program. Evergreen offers athletic and merit scholarships and is a **WUE** participant.

Study Away

Evergreen students usually have four or five faculty-led interdisciplinary study abroad programs to choose from each year and student exchanges with partner universities in Japan, South Korea, and Denmark.

Interdisciplinary Programs

The word interdisciplinary shows up repeatedly on college and university websites and in course and program descriptions. Almost every higher education institution advertises one or more interdisciplinary programs and mentions interdisciplinary perspectives, curricula, and research.

These institutions are recognizing that the technological revolution is demanding that graduates have more than one kind of skill, and have experience in thinking across disciplines, if they want to compete in today's job market. As a result, the number of Interdisciplinary Studies graduates in the workforce is growing rapidly.

There is considerable variation in the design, structure, and implementation of such programs, but the main factors that have driven this trend are summed up in a **2005 National Academies** report called **Facilitating Interdisciplinary Research*** as:

1. The inherent complexity of nature and society
2. The desire to explore problems and questions that are not confined to a single discipline
3. The need to solve social problems
4. The need to produce revolutionary insights and generative technologies.

*https://doi.org/10.3152/147154406781775841

Evergreen State College Basic Statistics

Undergraduate Enrollment	Freshman Class Enrollment	Institution Total Enrollment	Female/Male Student Ratio	Female/Male Faculty Ratio	Student/ Faculty Ratio
1,849	234	2,116	62/48	56/44	14/1
# of 1st Year Applications	**# of 1st Year Women Admitted**	**# of 1st Year Men Admitted**	**# of Transfer Students Admitted**	**Overall Yield**	**% of Out-of-State Students**
1,111	703	399	551	21%	15%
% Students Living in Campus After 1st Year	**Fraternity/ Sorority Participation**	**% Students Receiving Need-based Aid**	**1st Year Students Retention Rate**	**% Classes Under 30**	**% Caucasian/ White Faculty**
22%	0	70%	60%	86%	73%
# Caucasian / White Students	**# Hispanic / Latinx Students**	**# Asian Students**	**# Black Students**	**# American Indian/ Alaskan, Hawaiian /Native Pacific Islander**	**# International Students**
1,132	221	61	96	100	6
In-State Tuition and Fees	**Room and Board Average**	**Out-of-State Tuition and Fees**	**Honors Program Cost**	**Honors Program Scholarship**	**Athletic Division**
$8,664	$10,420	$29,172	n/a	n/a	NAIA

Notes:

Idaho State University

Pocatello, Idaho / www. isu.edu

This accessible and supportive state university is noted for its comprehensive programs and innovative research in the health sciences and technology.

Location

Pocatello, a city of 55,500 in the rural mountainous southeastern corner of the state, two hours west of Jackson WY, and two hours north of Salt Lake City, UT, is known as the **Gateway to the Northwest**.

At an elevation of 4449 ft., outdoor recreation options are abundant, especially for climbing, mountain biking, hiking, and winter sports. The city's geothermal hot springs are open year-round.

Fishing, Idaho

Pocatello's population lacks significant diversity, but the historic downtown has specialty shops, farmers and crafters markets, and a weekly art walk, and hosts a summer concert series and various festivals. There are bars and brew pubs, some of which have music, multiple restaurants and fast food places, and a shopping mall.

Pocatello gets a good forty-nine inches of snow annually, but is otherwise dry and mostly sunny with average temperatures in the high 80s in summer and low 40s in winter.

Community

Students comment that the ISU community is supportive, welcoming, and generally conservative. The student population of ISU includes 5600 full time and almost 4000 part-time undergraduates.

Although a majority of ISU students claim some affiliation with the Church of Latter Day Saints, there is also a Catholic Student Center and other religious clubs on campus, but no academic religion department.

ISU offers a seven-week **Bengal Bridge** program that helps students, especially first generation students, transition into college with the skills they need for success, while earning general education credits.

Pond Student Union serves as the community center for the University. The Union consists of three floors that house the campus bookstore, student government and organization offices, Outdoor Adventure Center, ISU Credit Union, Student Affairs Office, bowling alley, movie theater, Veterans Sanctuary, LEAD Center, and numerous conference rooms.

Academics

With its relatively small undergraduate population and 13:1 student to faculty ratio, classes at ISU tend to be small, and many hands-on learning opportunities are available. Students report that faculty members and administrative staff are supportive and professors are good at sharing their passion for their fields of expertise.

ISU is Idaho's lead institution in health professions and medical education, and over thirty percent of degrees earned are health profession related. The range of **Health Sciences** programs is impressive and covers undergraduate to Ph.D. studies in many specialties.

The University's undergraduate academic offerings are divided into colleges and schools, with concentrations in the fields of Arts and Letters, Business, Health, Education, Pharmacy, Science and Engineering, Technology, Health Sciences, Nursing, Performing Arts, and Rehabilitation and Communication Sciences. At the College of Technology, ISU's **Energy Systems Technology and Education Center** coordinates the nuclear energy education and training for technicians in a nine-state region. The University's **Research and**

Innovation in Science and Engineering Complex has a High Power Laser/Optics Laboratory, Imaging Laboratory, and a Human Interactive Environment Simulation Laboratory.

Honors Students follow an interdisciplinary curriculum and have living learning community housing and scholarships.

With a relatively new Bachelor of Arts degree in choreography and performance, ISU's School of Performing Arts offers majors in music, theatre, and dance that utilize the **Stephens Performing Arts Center's** state of the art facilities. These include a grand concert hall, two theaters, studios, and classrooms.

Recreational Activities and Residential Life

The **Associated Students of ISU** has responsibility for encouraging and coordinating student participation and representation in student affairs and handles funding for student clubs and organizations. It also has a judicial branch that deals with certain student infractions and a duty to actively represent students on issues and problems that arise within the community.

ISU's **Student Recreation Center** offers 100,000 sq. ft. of space for the main gym plus new facilities. It includes racquetball courts, an auxiliary gym, a track, climbing wall, a spinning/multi-purpose room, weight and endurance facilities, an indoor track, classrooms, and four indoor tennis courts. The swimming pool is currently out of service until a long term fix for aging problems is found.

In addition to Intramurals, students can participate in competitive rodeo, which uses the County event center's indoor and outdoor arenas. Other competitive clubs include Baseball, Climbing, Judo, Men's Rugby, Sport Shooting, Tennis, and Volleyball. The **Outdoor Adventure Center** caters to all interests and levels, provides equipment and repairs, and an extensive library of books, guides, and maps. The Center also sponsors a **Cooperative Wilderness Handicapped Outdoor Group**. ISU varsity athletes compete in the Big Sky Conference at NCAA Div. I level in five men's sports and eight women's sports and at Div. II in Men's Rugby.

First year students are offered traditional residential housing but can move into the innovative **Rendezvous Hall** complex that has suite style living and great common spaces for programs, classes, and dining after that. Food choices at ISU get mixed reviews from students.

Financial Aid

ISU is a **WUE** Institution. Scholarship aid includes athletic grants and academic merit, talent, and service scholarships.

Study Away

ISU participates in the National Student Exchange with other US universities and has partner organizations and institutions in many other countries that provide study abroad programs.

Cooperative Wilderness Handicapped Outdoor Group

Since 1981 volunteers have managed, raised funds for, and designed an innovative outdoor recreation program at ISU that is inclusive of all abilities.

With the deep interest in health and wellness professions at the ISU, this program draws student volunteers from all academic departments.

CW HOG provides challenging outdoor adventures in a supportive environment and has developed a supportive network for people with and without disabilities.

The program builds ties between individuals with disabilities and other community members and educates the public in accepting and valuing people with disabilities.

From adaptive-friendly whitewater rafting to cross country skiing, soaking in the nearby hot springs, social dinner parties, and trips to places like Yellowstone, the CW HOG group ensures there is something for all levels of ability, skill, and fitness.

Idaho State University Basic Statistics

Undergraduate Enrollment	Freshman Class Enrollment	Institution Total Enrollment	Female/Male Student Ratio	Female/Male Faculty Ratio	Student/ Faculty Ratio
9,831	1,167	12,157	59/41	49/51	13/1
# of 1st Year Applications	**# of 1st Year Women Admitted**	**# of 1st Year Men Admitted**	**# of Transfer Students Admitted**	**Overall Yield**	**% of Out-of-State Students**
4.495	2,603	1,885	740	33%	10%
% Students Living in Campus After 1st Year	**Fraternity/ Sorority Participation**	**% Students Receiving Need-based Aid**	**1st Year Students Retention Rate**	**% Classes Under 30**	**% Caucasian/ White Faculty**
12%	0	66%	67%	86%	81%
# Caucasian / White Students	**# Hispanic / Latinx Students**	**# Asian Students**	**# Black Students**	**# American Indian/ Alaskan, Hawaiian /Native Pacific Islander**	**# International Students**
8,830	1.527	199	147	212	226
In-State Tuition and Fees	**Room and Board Average**	**Out-of-State Tuition and Fees**	**Honors Program Cost**	**Honors Program Scholarship**	**Athletic Division**
$7,872	$8,370	$25,326	0	$1,000 1st yr.	NCAA I

Notes:

Lewis and Clark State College

Lewiston, Idaho / www.lcsc.edu

This state line and riverside public college welcomes almost all applicants and supports their path to success in a wide variety of vocational, technical, and academic programs in a safe learning environment.

Location

Idaho's Lewiston seaport on the Snake River is the farthest inland port on the west coast and right on the state line between Idaho and Washington. Surrounded by mountains, rivers, and the scenic rolling hills of the Palouse, the area provides residents with year around outdoor sports and recreation opportunities in a semi-arid climate with short winters. The regional airport is served by two commercial airlines.

This conservative city of 33,000 has a safe hometown feeling but is lacking in diversity. The community is appreciative of its very affordable and highly respected home town college. Students report that they get used to the odor of the local paper plant, which is a major economic driver in the region.

Lewiston has a golf course, an aquatics center, bowling lanes, and an ice arena. A variety of restaurants and shopping options are available. Local businesses and recreation facilities offer student discounts.

Community

This public college welcomes almost all applicants and supports their path to success in a wide variety of vocational, technical, and academic programs.

LCSE's undergraduate population includes 2100 full time and 895 part time undergraduates. Among the full time students, men are well outnumbered by women, while the part time students are more equally divided as to gender.

The College's mission is to offer a unique and safe learning environment that prepares students for successful leadership and responsibility as citizens and encourages lifelong learning. With a focus on providing transformative educational experiences, the College has ample resources for students who need academic or tutoring support.

Students describe the LCSC community as quiet and comforting but with a strong school spirit. The **Associated Students of LCSC** organization serves as the student government and voice of the Student Body.

Academics

LCSC offers over 130 Degree and Certificate programs, including AAS, B.A., and B.S. degrees. The small classes, hands-on learning, and positive student-faculty interaction, are welcome features of most LCSC courses. The College also has an extensive online course catalog, so you will want to ask whether your chosen program will include any online courses.

The College has three distinct schools, the School of Career and Technical Education, the School of Liberal Arts and Sciences, and the School of Professional Studies. 25% of certificates and degrees are awarded in the Nursing and Health Professions programs, and 33% are earned in Liberal Arts and Education fields.

LCSC offers Sport Management and Sports Media Studies with related Kinesiology and Exercise Science programs. Business and Technology programs are also popular. By the Fall of 2022, the College intends to offer a four year degree in Cybersecurity, utilizing the two **Security Operations Centers** on the campus for hands-on training. This is part of the college's plan to focus on educating and training students for high-demand careers.

Many LCSC faculty members are active researchers as well as teachers. Biology professors recently secured a grant to do wastewater and sewage testing to detect transmissible disease using robotic equipment and they are training students as research assistants on the project. Most students engage in a research project in their senior year.

The new **Schweitzer CTE Center** is an 86,000 sq. ft. facility housing seven **Technical and Industrial**

Division programs. These include auto mechanics, CNC machining, industrial electronics, maintenance, and millwright technology programs, heating, ventilation, air conditioning, and refrigeration technologies.

LCSC encourages experiential learning such as internships and field courses. For instance, the Psychology program offers courses in which the students must serve internships with local agencies to gain critical and practical experience. The Division of Physical, Life, Movement, and Sport Sciences has several well-equipped labs that offer students a wide range of options for research and hands-on professional skills development.

Recreational Activities and Residential Life

Over fifty student-led organizations on the LCSC campus encourage students to explore new fun opportunities and develop a sense of belonging in the campus community. Multicultural and Native American organizations, a Latina sorority, a Gender and Sexuality Alliance, a Theater troupe, a Comedy Club, and a Rodeo and Equine Club are among the options. Students operate a radio station, a newspaper, and a biannual student-edited literary magazine called the **Talking River Review.**

About a third of first year students live in campus housing, but most find other accommodations after that, including in college-owned apartments and houses off campus. The residence halls foster the development of shared fun and friendships.

LCSC has a large **Fitness Center**, lots of intramurals, and an active **Outdoor Program**. A tri-level venue, the **P1FCU Activity Cente**r, has three full-sized basketball/volleyball courts, classrooms, a dance and exercise studio, and athletic training facilities.

Five men's and five women's very competitive varsity teams compete in the NAIA Cascade Collegiate conference. LCSC's renowned baseball program, which has seen many players drafted to professional leagues, and gained many national championships, uses **Harris Field** baseball park, an on-campus venue with seating for 5,000.

LCSC is Idaho's most affordable public higher education institution. The **College Assistance Migrant Financial Aid Program** helps students with family backgrounds in migrant and seasonal farm work enter and succeed in college. In addition to the **WUE** discount for out of state students, LCSC offers other out of state scholarships and discount tuition for any Asotin County, WA students.

Study Away

LCSC has an endowed scholarship for foreign language study abroad. The Anthropology Department offers a three-week **Cultural Anthropology Field School** in Ecuador, involving community service, research, and language immersion. The college partners with the **National Student Exchange** program.

College Assistance Migrant Program (CAMP)

The **College Assistance Migrant Program** is a unique educational program funded by the U.S. Department of Education through competitive five-year grants awarded to colleges and universities. The CAMP programs provide access to college education and training for students who have qualifying migrant and seasonal farm work backgrounds.

The CAMP grant awardees such as LCSC use the grant funds to provide individual support for these students through tutoring, mentoring, internship, financial aid assistance, and career exploration opportunities. CAMP grantees can also use this grant funding for follow-up services for students who complete their first year.

Although federal CAMP financial aid is only offered through the student's first academic year of college, LCSC has committed to providing academic support through graduation.

Other PNW CAMP five year grant awardees for 2021 include Central Washington U, Portland CC, and Skagit Valley College Education Association.

Lewis and Clark State College Basic Statistics

Undergraduate Enrollment	Freshman Class Enrollment	Institution Total Enrollment	Female/Male Student Ratio	Female/Male Faculty Ratio	Student/ Faculty Ratio
3,710	394	3,711	64/36	61/39	15/1
# of 1st Year Applications	**# of 1st Year Women Admitted**	**# of 1st Year Men Admitted**	**# of Transfer Students Admitted**	**Overall Yield**	**% of Out-of-State Students**
1,580	971	609	511	25%	21%
% Students Living in Campus After 1st Year	**Fraternity/ Sorority Participation**	**% Students Receiving Need-based Aid**	**1st Year Students Retention Rate**	**% Classes Under 30**	**% Caucasian/ White Faculty**
--	0	66%	63%	95%	100%
# Caucasian / White Students	**# Hispanic / Latinx Students**	**# Asian Students**	**# Black Students**	**# American Indian/ Alaskan, Hawaiian /Native Pacific Islander**	**# International Students**
2,855	313	42	32	98	58
In-State Tuition and Fees	**Room and Board Average**	**Out-of-State Tuition and Fees**	**Honors Program Cost**	**Honors Program Scholarship**	**Athletic Division**
$6,996	$8,460	$20,252	n/a	n/a	NAIA

Notes:

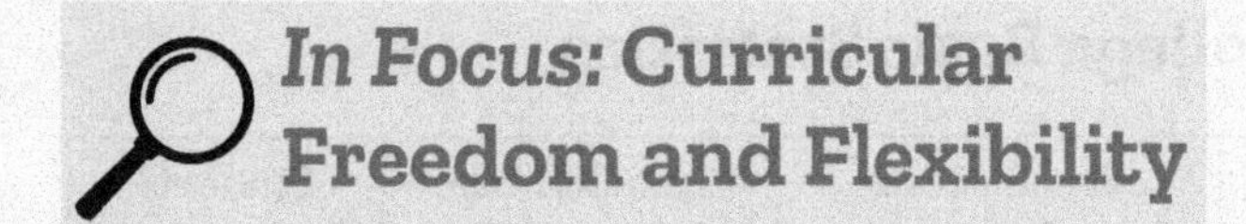

In Focus: Curricular Freedom and Flexibility

The Traditional Curriculum

The traditional design of a four year undergraduate curriculum involves a specific core of required courses, sometimes called General Studies or Distribution Requirements. These are meant to give the student a broad educational foundation before choosing a specific major with its own set of requirements.

Most students entering college do expect to have a structured and pre-determined pathway to a college degree. Only at the largest institutions where required courses may fill up quickly, or not be offered in the time period a student needs for graduation in four years, do these required courses and pre-requisites sometimes pose a serious problem. Very determined and exceptionally self-reliant students can petition to design their own major at almost all higher education institutions.

The Self-determined Curriculum

There are also some colleges that offer students a more flexible curriculum, one that allows students to explore far more freely, and to self-determine their academic pathways. These less traditional institutions strongly emphasize cross-disciplinary study, self-designed majors, and experiential options for development of professional skills. They do, however, require self-discipline and purposeful decision making.

Here are some examples of institutions that allow exceptional freedom of choice:

- At **Quest University** students spend their first two years taking a choice of multidisciplinary foundation courses. The Block Plan schedule requires one very intensive class every three and half weeks. By 3rd year students begin to home in on one key question related to their interests and take related courses to explore that idea.

  The selected question becomes the main topic of a self-designed deep research and creative presentation Keystone Project focused on answering that question and this can involve collaborative research with a faculty member, off campus research and field study, and publication.

- **The College of Idaho's** unique **PEAKS** program requires one major and three minors. Instead of checking off a list of core requirements this curriculum allows students to explore a range of interests while engaging in a broad liberal arts education.

  The only required minor is called Professional Foundations and Enhancements and is focused on acquiring critical skills and foundational knowledge for both academic and professional success.

- **The Fairhaven College of Interdisciplinary Studies** at **Western Washington University** focuses on developing students' critical consciousness through exploration and on intentional learning across disciplines, along with foundational skills, independent study and experiential projects. Courses are in small seminar classes and there is strong mentoring. Self-designed interdisciplinary majors are strongly supported.

Independent Majors

Independent majors are an option for the intellectually curious, self-motivated and well-disciplined learner who wants to pursue deep learning.

Willamette University is one example of the PNW institutions that give students the option of designing their own majors. Typically this need arises when a student's interests cross disciplinary boundaries in ways that are not addressed by the institution's current major choices.

Each institution will require certain distribution and number of credits and generally an integrative senior capstone project or thesis. It also requires close work with a sponsoring faculty member at every stage of planning, research, and development.

Whitman College also allows the design of an independent major in a concentrated study of an area that crosses two or more disciplines, if no comparable program is available at the institution. At Whitman this requires at least three faculty members to serve as an Individually Planned Major committee with which the student develops a proposal and schedule of coursework prior to the start of the student's junior year.

University of Washington has a well-developed **Individualized Learning Plan** with very specific guidelines. It requires approval of a detailed learning plan from key departments and a faculty advisor agreement. Students may not double major with Individualized Studies. If approved, the Learning Plan then becomes the graduation plan. If rejected the student may not reapply for an Individualized major.

Independent Study

Most colleges and Universities allow a limited number of credits to be earned in self-designed independent study courses under the supervision of a faculty advisor. Rules and credit limitations vary from one institution to another and some internship and study away programs can fall into this category.

Advantages and Disadvantages of Independent Study Plans

What It Can Offer

- ✔ Opportunity for in-depth research experience.
- ✔ Opportunity for valuable student-mentor relationship with a faculty member(s).
- ✔ Can be a creative culmination of several years themed or interdisciplinary coursework.
- ✔ May offer exposure to advanced study area not covered by standard coursework.
- ✔ Will require learning advanced research and professional communication skills and protocols, how to write proposals, and how to analyze and report results.
- ✔ May provide opportunities for practical hands-on lab experience, field work, internships, and co-op employment in the student's area of study.
- ✔ May provide opportunity to present original work at professional conferences and symposiums.
- ✔ May provide opportunity to be acknowledged as a contributor in a published academic paper with mentor or other faculty.
- ✔ Can enhance student's resume for post college employment or graduate program admissions.

What It Will Demand

- ✔ Demands strong motivation and self-discipline.
- ✔ Requires careful pre-planning on choice of topic, design of project, and how it will fit into requirements and timeline for graduation.
- ✔ Demands a serious commitment of time and energy that may conflict with other interests and activities.
- ✔ Will not tolerate procrastination well.
- ✔ Requires regular communication and good rapport with mentor(s).
- ✔ Student's course schedule will need to offer the flexibility required to initiate and complete the project within a specific period of time.
- ✔ Can require incorporation of a summer research period.
- ✔ If an independent study project is substituting for an advanced standard course, the student may miss out on broader coverage of the field of study and opportunities to discuss different perspectives on issues or problems, take part in team projects, and meet others with similar interests.

University of Montana

Missoula, Montana / www.umt.edu

The University of Montana offers a lively campus, a thriving community, outstanding STEM and Business programs, and a natural landscape that invites and challenges outdoor enthusiasts.

Location

Missoula is proud of its 400 acres of parklands and 22 miles of trails. With an elevation of 3200 ft. and sitting at the confluence of three rivers, Missoula is surrounded by steep mountains with abundant wildlife and beautiful scenery. Near Glacier National Park, Missoula has cold and moderately snowy winters, hot and dry summers, and short, crisp springs and autumns.

The metro area population is about 120,000 and growing. The main economic drivers include the University, schools, health care, and tourism. The city is the cultural hub of the metro area and home to a state museum of art and culture and a well-known children's theater academy. With an eclectic range of restaurants and bistros and several breweries, downtown Missoula has a lively pub and dining scene.

Community

One look at UM's campus and the amount of square footage devoted to athletics, including the 25,200 seat football stadium, suggests that this institution attracts students and faculty who enjoy the sense of team spirit and community cohesion they find here.

UM draws almost a third of its undergraduate students from out of state, primarily from the neighboring PNW states and California. Students comment on the warm acceptance and faculty and staff support they have experienced at UM.

UM is working on fostering and recruiting for diversity, equity, and inclusion. While the diversity of the undergraduate population has improved, the faculty remains almost 95% white.

A four-day **Freshman Wilderness Experience** not only introduces new students to the area's varied wild places, rivers, and mountains but also provides a chance to bond with new friends by sharing fun and challenging adventures.

Academics

UM, as the state's flagship university, divides its undergraduate academics into six distinct colleges. These include the College of Humanities and Sciences, the Colleges of Education, Forestry and Conservation, Health, Business, and Arts and Media, along with the **Davidson Honors College**. **Missoula College**, a two-year unit of the University, provides occupational and technical education.

The University recognizes that the undergraduate programs need to incorporate more interdisciplinary options and is working on enhancing the synergy within and between these units. A **Grand Challenges Initiative** at UM focuses on integrating broad themes of global relevance into the curriculum and encouraging students to get direct experience in addressing critical issues of significance to them. This is indicative of UM's push for curricular innovation. The University seeks to meet the needs of students facing a changing work climate that now demands a broader skill set and a creative, agile, and collaborative mindset.

Social justice, sustainability, and public health are major research areas at UM, and experiential learning opportunities are available in all areas. The Visual and Performing Arts students are a vibrant and creative community for arts and culture. Their productions and performances enhance life for the campus community and the residents of the larger Missoula metro area communities.

Business, Management, and Marketing are among the most popular degrees at UM. Pre-law students have an excellent acceptance rate into law schools, and accounting students tend to do very well on their CPA exams. The School of Journalism is also nationally recognized for excellence, as are the Environmental Studies and Wildlife Biology programs and the Pharmacy program.

Recreational Activities and Residential Life

The large and well-equipped **Fitness and Recreation Center**, one of several LEED-certified buildings on the UM campus, includes a climbing wall, squash and racquetball courts, and saunas. The Outdoor program, golf course, 25 yd. competition pool, intramural practice fields, and **Schreiber Gym,** all cater to intramural and Club Sports teams and individual use. UM varsity athletes compete in NCAA Division 1 in fifteen sports and have their own premier athletics performance center.

The **University Center** is a hub for all events, clubs, services, and other activities, including a **Gaming Den**. The 146 student organizations include everything from professional and identity-based organizations to a backcountry hunter and anglers group, an Indigenous Storytelling Club, Telemark Skiing Club, Zootown Cabaret, and more. The student newspaper, radio station, a music recording studio, literary magazine, and the Associated Students organization all offer opportunities for involvement, leadership, and skills development for interested students.

Eight fraternities and five sororities are well established at UM and contribute to the community service and social activities. Alcohol has been a problem at UM and the institution has a party school reputation.

Students with fewer than 30 credits must live on campus, and there are many options in the eight residential halls. Students can choose living learning communities with themes such as gender-inclusive, honors, pre-health, and outdoor recreation. Suite and apartment living is available for older students. The multiple campus dining venues use 3000 lbs. of fresh produce grown in the University's campus gardens.

Financial Aid

A new **Payne Family Impact Scholarship** will help Montana residents caught in the middle-income financial gap access higher education at UM. The University is a **WUE** participant.

Study Away

UM's **Global Engagement Office** is active in promoting and providing university-wide programming with International and Global themes and related study abroad and internship experiences. UM has Partner Universities and Student Exchange programs and offers faculty-led study trips. The **Mansfield Center** hosts international exchange programs and supports a unique study abroad program on climate change in the Mekong Delta of Vietnam and scholarships for study abroad elsewhere.

Gaming Rooms

Due to student demand, Gaming rooms or dens have become ubiquitous at colleges and universities. Whether a student utilizes these facilities to escape reality for a while and de-stress or just have fun with friends, game rooms are an attractive amenity.

For the average college student, video games are as much a part of life as studying and partying. Game Dens or game rooms at these institutions will often offer more than state of the art video game equipment, however. Many will have a pool table, table tennis, air hockey, and even a lounge area for study or socializing.

Colleges and universities are also beginning to sponsor competitive Esports teams to play in tournaments and support campus-based chapters of Esport leagues. The **National Association of Collegiate Esports** is a non-profit organization that encourages Varsity Esports development at colleges and universities and offers some scholarship aid for NACE student-athletes.

The University of Montana is among the several PNW higher education institutions that are affiliates and competitors in the NACE Varsity Division.

University of Montana Basic Statistics

Undergraduate Enrollment	Freshman Class Enrollment	Institution Total Enrollment	Female/Male Student Ratio	Female/Male Faculty Ratio	Student/ Faculty Ratio
5,685	771	12,694	54/46	--	19/1
# of 1st Year Applications	**# of 1st Year Women Admitted**	**# of 1st Year Men Admitted**	**# of Transfer Students Admitted**	**Overall Yield**	**% of Out-of-State Students**
5,380	2,990	2,163	--	25%	35%
% Students Living in Campus After 1st Year	**Fraternity/ Sorority Participation**	**% Students Receiving Need-based Aid**	**1st Year Students Retention Rate**	**% Classes Under 30**	**% Caucasian/ White Faculty**
32%	5%	59%	68%	70%	--
# Caucasian / White Students	**# Hispanic / Latinx Students**	**# Asian Students**	**# Black Students**	**# American Indian/ Alaskan, Hawaiian /Native Pacific Islander**	**# International Students**
71%	4.88%	6.77%	1%	4.27%	--
In-State Tuition and Fees	**Room and Board Average**	**Out-of-State Tuition and Fees**	**Honors Program Cost**	**Honors Program Scholarship**	**Athletic Division**
$7,430	$11,780	$14.811	0	varies	NCAA Div. I

Notes:

Montana Technological University

Butte-Silver Bow, Montana / www.mtech.edu

Students come to Montana Tech, the state's Special Focus STEM University, because of its reputation for high levels of professional job placement, great return on investment, small class sizes, abundant research opportunities, and valuable industry connections.

Location

At an elevation of 5817 ft. and nearly surrounded by the Beaver Head/Dearlodge National Forest, the mountain town of Butte is where the Continental Divide National Scenic Trail (CDNST) offers 13 trailheads to pristine vistas and open areas.

Outdoor recreation and adventures abound, as do the old mining sites, including a huge open-pit Superfund site on the east side of the small city.

Famous for its historical past as a booming mining community where fortunes were made and many ethnic groups came to work, the area has warm, dry summers and cold winters that average 53 inches of snow.

With its mix of ethnicities and union worker legacy, the residents are noted for being somewhat progressive. The Butte experience is enhanced by numerous micro-breweries and artisan micro-distilleries of small batch spirits. Residents and students also get to enjoy an unusual range of ethnic restaurants, including The Pekin Noodle Parlor, the oldest family-owned, continuously operating Chinese restaurant in the U.S.

Community

The Montana Tech campus is perched on a hill on the city's west side. "We love over-achievers" is a phrase you'll find on the Montana Tech website, and students enroll here because of its academic and professional reputation. One of the few PNW universities with more men than women students, Montana Tech also draws about ten percent of its students from other countries, primarily Saudi Arabia, Kuwait, and Canada. There is a **Buddy Program** here, which pairs up current students with incoming foreign exchange students.

Students tend to be seriously focused on their fields of study and very practical about their reasons for enrolling at MT. However, they still find time to be engaged with various clubs and organizations, play sports at whatever level they enjoy, and take advantage of the outdoor recreational options.

The small student body size and close engagement with faculty in intimate and challenging classes offer students a sense of being in a community of like-minded, purposeful, and curious doers who seek ways to make a difference in their chosen professions and fields of interest.

Academics

Montana Tech started as the state's School of Mines and Engineering and has expanded to include a College of Letters, Sciences, and Professional Studies and become Montana's only Special Focus STEM University. MT also incorporates the two year **Highlands College** that offers certificate and Associate degrees with a seamless transfer option and university housing for its students.

Montana Tech boasts that it offers "hands-on and industry-ready" education, and its outstanding record of job placement and exceptionally high return on investment bears that out. The student to faculty ratio is 14:1. Students describe a more personal connection with all the faculty and staff due to small class sizes and student population. While MT's engineering departments are consistently listed as among the best, its nursing program was just recently named Best Nursing School in Montana.

MT offers one of only six degrees in the U.S. specializing in Extractive Metallurgy & Mineral Processing Engineering. There are also newly accredited Civil and Environmental Engineering programs that are increasing students' options. MT's Environmental Design teams are also award winners.

MT's five research centers include the **Montana Bureau of Mines and Geology,** the **Center for Environmental**

Remediation, the **Center for Assessment and Advanced Materials Processing,** a **High Performance Computing Cluster,** and the **Underground Mine Education Center.** The Sciences and Math programs are remarkable at MT, and both the Business Tech and Management and the Cyber Security programs attract students to MT.

Fieldwork, internships, lab research, and relevant industry exposure are significant elements of the Montana Tech academic experience in all departments. The University boasts of state of the art facilities and equipment and close industry ties. MT's Career Fairs bring employers from some of the world's leading industries and businesses to campus to meet, interview, and recruit students for internships and employment.

Recreational Activities and Residential Living

Students at MT have plenty of options to do more than study. The outdoors beckons with hiking and biking trails right out the door, and water sports, rock climbing, hot springs, caverns, and winter skiing are easily accessible. On campus, the **Recreation Center** offers a gym, racquetball courts, fitness center, a 25 meter pool, dance studio, classrooms, and a performance lab.

Clubs and organizations are numerous, including professions-related ones such as the Society of Women Engineers, service-based like Engineers without Borders, and academic interest clubs such as the NASA Robotics Mining Competition Club. Club sports and social-based clubs, include fly fishing, skiing and snowboarding, dancing, and cultural exchange groups. Varsity athletes compete at NAIA Division I in the Frontier Conference in six sports, including golf.

First year students are required to live on campus. There are traditional and suite style room options among the three residence halls, one of which is a new living learning center with a majority of single rooms. All provide plenty of socializing space, kitchens, and laundry amenities. The new **Living Learning Center** is connected to the **Student Success Center,** which offers tutoring, private study rooms, computer labs and social spaces.

Financial Aid

Montana residents can apply for an array of merit scholarships. Montana Tech is a **WUE** school. 92% of first time students received some level of financial aid. MT's most competitive scholarships are the **Marie Moebus Presidential Scholarships** which give tuition waiver awards. Varsity sports related student aid is also available.

Study Away

Montana Tech offers 250 study abroad programs in 60 countries and has student, faculty, and research exchange agreements with multiple partner universities.

Society of Women Engineers (SWE)

SWE is a non-profit organization (SWE.org) that has given women engineers a place and voice within the engineering industry for over seven decades. Their mission involves encouraging young women to consider engineering careers, and they offer training and development, networking opportunities, career fairs, and scholarships.

College students who join an SWE chapter at their institution can benefit from SWE support and training to successfully transition to the engineering workforce. A Collegiate to Career membership only requires one $50 fee for the student's entire college career and first year of employment after that.

Joining SWE at college gives students a cohort of women students with interests in engineering, technology, and computing, plus opportunities to get advice and guidance from practicing engineers.

SWE hosts the world's largest career fair for women in engineering and awards more than $800,000 a year in scholarships and scholarships are open to all candidates who identify as female.

Montana Technological University Basic Statistics

Undergraduate Enrollment	Freshman Class Enrollment	Institution Total Enrollment	Female/Male Student Ratio	Female/Male Faculty Ratio	Student/ Faculty Ratio
1,779	324	2,339	42/58	44/56	14/1
# of 1st Year Applications	**# of 1st Year Women Admitted**	**# of 1st Year Men Admitted**	**# of Transfer Students Admitted**	**Overall Yield**	**% of Out-of-State Students**
1,000	300	700	69	25%	15%
% Students Living in Campus After 1st Year	**Fraternity/ Sorority Participation**	**% Students Receiving Need-based Aid**	**1st Year Students Retention Rate**	**% Classes Under 30**	**% Caucasian/ White Faculty**
--	n/a	--	79%	61%	69%
# Caucasian / White Students	**# Hispanic / Latinx Students**	**# Asian Students**	**# Black Students**	**# American Indian/ Alaskan, Hawaiian /Native Pacific Islander**	**# International Students**
1916	79	30	21	63	57
In-State Tuition and Fees	**Room and Board Average**	**Out-of-State Tuition and Fees**	**Honors Program Cost**	**Honors Program Scholarship**	**Athletic Division**
$7,580*	$10,741	$23,210*	0	varies	NAIA

*2021-22

Notes:

University of Montana Western

Dillon, Montana / www.umwestern.edu

Montana Western, the only public four-year university in the U.S. offering a full-year block schedule, believes in experiential learning through real-world educational experiences, internships, and projects, many of which involve community service.

Location

The town of Dillon sits at an elevation of 5,240 ft. in the extreme southwest of Montana and was a stopover for the Lewis and Clark Expedition in 1805. Dillon still serves as a hub of activity for the area and as tourist headquarters for those planning to explore and recreate on some of the most pristine and scenic lands in the state.

Beaverhead River, Dillon, MT

Visitors can hike a portion of the nearby Continental Divide Trail, enjoy the two hot springs, and experience the area's great fly fishing. As a result of the strong tourist interest, Dillon offers an abundant number of dining and lodging options, a craft brewery, and even a Patagonia outlet for students and faculty of the University to enjoy.

Summers are pleasant and dry, and winters are fairly mild, with only 20 inches of snow on average.

Community

Montana Western's 1200+ students enjoy a supportive and engaging community environment at this unique public university. They comment on the friendliness, not only of students and staff but also of the town residents and businesses who welcome them. The Block Plan (**Experience One**) keeps students busily immersed in each course and on project assignments during each eighteen-day block period. Students work closely with their professors and as cohorts in a spirit of collaboration and exploration. The University is committed to a sustainable environment, and its buildings are heated by biomass.

With its strong focus on hands-on experiential learning, The Block Plan allows time in each course for faculty to utilize multi-day field trips, intensive lab research, community service projects, include guest speakers and clinicians in their courses, or take students to conferences where they can present their research.

As an historic 125 year-old institution established in a relatively conservative rural western mining, farm, and ranching region, the University takes the lead in addressing community issues of diversity and inclusion. About seventeen percent of its students identify as other than white, and a quarter of students come from out of state. The **Multi-Cultural Center** offers programs, lectures, movies, cultural celebrations, discussion groups and social events to increase understanding, promote inclusion, and inspire critical thinking about diversity.

Academics

UMW offers both popular associate degrees, and four year degrees, and many require an internship or cooperative education experience. Among both levels of degrees are two that are not offered anywhere else in the U.S. These are a Fine Arts degree with a specialization in **Scientific Glassblowing** that utilizes the fully equipped glass facilities on campus, and a demanding degree in **Natural Horsemanship** which offers concentrations in management, business, psychology, science, and instruction. UMW's Horsemanship students have recently done teaching internships abroad.

UMW's Education Department draws the most students and offers a full range of education degrees and certificates. The new **Dennis & Phyllis Washington Foundation Model Classroom** gives pre-service teacher candidates experience in planning and implementing entire units of instruction that they put into use in the Rural Fridays program. This program brings elementary students from one and two-room rural schools, and home-schooled children, to the campus each week for a day of innovative instruction and experience with peers of their own age.

The Environmental Science Department states that its classrooms "have no walls." The mountains and valleys of southwest Montana serve as a natural lab to work on real projects that make a positive difference in the quality of the environment. Long hours in the field, overnight trips, research for non-profit projects, and even classes that involve traveling abroad help students build impressive portfolios that aid in UMW's 90% job placement record.

The Business and Technology Department emphasizes entrepreneurship for small businesses and related technology. Hands-on team projects and problem-based learning and internships are emphasized. A **Fourth Year Option** in this department allows students to complete their senior year courses online while starting their own business or while completing an internship or co-op experience. New minors include Farm and Ranch Operations, Outdoor Guide, and Wildlife Outfitters Management.

UMW's **Honors Program** focuses on interdisciplinary studies and fosters collaboration and discussions. Honors students have opportunities for independent research and creative endeavors, and qualified students are offered scholarships.

Recreational Activities and Residential Life

UMW has four residence halls and one family housing complex with all the usual amenities. An older hall has suites and apartment style options. Residents are required to pay for a full meal plan. Students report that the campus dining is excellent and also mention the wide array of downtown restaurants available.

The **Associated Students of UMW** student-run organization serves as the voice for students and advocates for their needs and interests. It also publishes a newsletter highlighting club events and activities and sponsors campus intramurals, including basketball, soccer, ultimate, and more. There are many funded campus clubs and groups active on campus. Students can get involved with others interested in music, skiing, vet science, gaming, and even draft horse driving.

UMW athletes compete in the NAIA and Frontier Conference in six men's and six women's sports, including rodeo, track and field, xcountry, football, volleyball and basketball.

Financial Aid

UWM's overall costs are very reasonable and UWM is a **WUE** participant. Some scholarships are only for Montana students. FSEOG grants are limited, so submit FAFSA and apply before Dec.1.

Study Away

The **Experience One** program offers opportunities to take faculty-led courses that include international travel and to arrange internships abroad for credit.

Scientific Glassblowing

The art of producing and repairing scientific glass containers and apparatuses suitable for scientific research and complex products requires technical precision and proficiency of the highest degree.

Scientific glass companies supply custom products for medical research laboratories and for scientific, photonic, solar, fiber optic, and semiconductor industries and require highly trained glassblowers.

Receiving instruction in this specialty can also bolster art students who want to develop a strong technical foundation in the principles of torch worked glass.

At the advanced level of scientific glassblowing, UWM students are introduced to lathe working techniques, exotic glasses, and the use of hydrogen as fuel and begin working on larger and more complex projects.

UWM students in this and other specialties can earn up to fifteen credits in an internship, or cooperative education work experience, to add on the job training to their portfolios and resumes.

University of Montana Western Basic Statistics

Undergraduate Enrollment	Freshman Class Enrollment	Institution Total Enrollment	Female/Male Student Ratio	Female/Male Faculty Ratio	Student/ Faculty Ratio
1,334	--	1,334	63/36	--	15:1
# of 1st Year Applications	**# of 1st Year Women Admitted**	**# of 1st Year Men Admitted**	**# of Transfer Students Admitted**	**Overall Yield**	**% of Out-of-State Students**
860	260	185	--	54%	25%
% Students Living in Campus After 1st Year	**Fraternity/ Sorority Participation**	**% Students Receiving Need-based Aid**	**1st Year Students Retention Rate**	**% Classes Under 30**	**% Caucasian/ White Faculty**
--	--	--	73%	100%	--
% Caucasian / White Students	**% Hispanic / Latinx Students**	**% Asian Students**	**% Black Students**	**% American Indian/ Alaskan, Hawaiian /Native Pacific Islander**	**% International Students**
79.4%	4.8%	.4%	1.6%	8%	.2%
In-State Tuition and Fees*	**Room and Board Average***	**Out-of-State Tuition and Fees***	**Honors Program Cost**	**Honors Program Scholarship**	**Athletic Division**
$5,875	$8,280	$17,684	--	varies	NAIA

Notes:

University of Oregon

Eugene, Oregon / www.uoregon.edu

U Oregon's focus on interdisciplinary collaboration and innovation, and options for engaging in research in cutting-edge facilities, draws both in state and out of state students to its vibrant campus and active social life.

Location

Eugene is situated on the southern end of the lush Willamette Valley and near the confluence of two rivers. Home to the state's flagship university, the city's residents enjoy a vibrant arts and education focused community in an urban/suburban setting with a population of about 160,000.

Situated just 61 miles from the Pacific coast, the climate is temperate with cool, wet, and often overcast winters and warm, dry summers. Portland is two hours to the North, and mountain skiing 2.5 hours to the East.

Downtown Eugene is busy with trendy pubs, coffee-houses, boutiques, an eclectic choice of restaurants, and a popular Saturday Artisans Market. The **Hult Center for the Performing Arts** serves as the region's major venue for events, musical concerts, and theatrical performances.

Community

UOregon has an undergraduate student population of 16,400 of which 56% are women and 43% come from out of state. The university community is openly progressive and generally accepting, friendly, and down to earth.

An **IntroDucktion** orientation for first year students gets students off to a good start and connected with university services and support. Students comment on the good lines of communication with faculty and staff and the fact that the city is so welcoming to the students.

Having fun on the way to a degree is a clear goal of many U Oregon students. There are enough parties available to land the university on the list of the top 20 party schools in the nation.

Students are very supportive of their highly competitive varsity sports teams and team colors and logos abound on game days.

Academics

UOregon has seven undergraduate divisions offering a total of over 300 different programs. These are the Colleges of Arts and Sciences, Business, Design, and Education, the School of Journalism and Communication, and the **Robert D Clark Honors College.** Interdisciplinary collaboration and innovation are well-established priorities at UO. Ambitious undergrads can engage in ground breaking research in facilities such as the **Phil and Penney Knight Campus for Accelerating Scientific Impact,** where major grants support outstanding faculty researchers.

UOregon has the largest full time music faculty in the Northwest. Thirty student ensembles, plus visiting artists, present around three hundred concerts a year in its two concert halls, the historic **Beall Concert Hall** and the modern multi-use **Aasen-Hull Hall.** The University's Dance program is large enough to have its own Dance Theater and the **Intermedia Music Technology Center** is an outstanding, well-equipped facility.

The most popular majors at UOregon have been in the Social Sciences, Communication, Journalism, and Business. Biological and Life Sciences, Psychology, Interdisciplinary Studies and Visual and Performing Arts are also very popular. This level of diversity, and the depth of academic opportunities, is one of the appeals of attending a larger institution. The majors in such fields as Biology, Computer Science, Earth Sciences, Geography, Mathematics, and Political Science offer multiple choices for **Concentrations** in areas of specific interest.

The University's **School of Global Studies and Languages** offers instruction in eighteen languages and engages students in the study of globally diverse cultures, histories, and communities. General social studies is another interdisciplinary program offering substantial flexibility and interesting Concentrations such as applied economics and globalization, or environment and policy. The **College of Design** offers Professional Studio Arts and Architecture and a Planning, Public Policy and Management program. The innovative **School of Journalism and Communication** is liberal arts based, flexible, and hands-on. Its new **Catalyst Journalism Project** focuses on investigative reporting and solutions-journalism to spark action and response.

Recreational Activities and Residential Life

First year students live on campus and housing choices include living learning and interest based communities, gender expansive, identity based, and one quiet community. **Honors College** students have an academic home in Chapman Hall and designated residential options. Food is rated healthy and bountiful. A 500 seat PNW Public Market is a new addition to UO's nine different dining facilities.

With approximately two hundred and fifty student organizations, twenty-eight intramural leagues, and forty competitive intercollegiate club sports, recreational and social engagement options are almost overwhelming at UOregon. Fraternities and sororities are popular and have historical ties to the University. The **Erb Memorial Union** is where student groups can meet, cultural events are held, a Computing Lab and tech service desk and the student newspaper offices are located, and where students can find services and information resources.

The LEED Platinum **Student Rec Center** is the hub for fitness, PE, and intramural sports and is a sustainable architecture and planning model. Varsity athletes compete at NCAA Division I level in the Pacific-12 Conference. Home games in the 54,000 seat **Autzen Stadium** can almost stop the town, drown out conversations, and then enliven the after-game party scene.

Financial Aid

Federal Pell Grant eligible Oregonians have 100 percent of their tuition and fees covered for up to 12 academic terms for undergraduate study through the **UO Pathway** program. Merit awards are based on GPA. The **UO Excellence** scholarship provides a limited number of awards to high achieving out of state students. The **Stamps Scholarship** is awarded to five top out of state applicants. UO is not a WUE school.

Study Away

UO's **GEO** program offers a full range of study abroad options including at Centers in London, Spain, and Italy. The **Freeman Fellowship** supports a Global Works internship in East and Southeast Asia. Faculty-led summer programs offer diverse field experiences, and need-based study abroad scholarships are available.

Concentrations

Concentrations ?? Minors ?? These closely related terms can be confusing. Let's clarify.

Minor: A Minor can be in any academic field, one closely related to your major or one in a seemingly unrelated area. Of course, we know that in today's world of interdisciplinary perspectives there are always overlaps to be found if you dig deep enough.

For instance, not long ago, someone majoring in performing arts might not have considered a minor in business, but be willing to let someone else handle that side of their career. Today, thanks to media coverage of stars, that performer might realize they need to know enough about business management and contracts to protect themselves against incompetence or fraud. So doing a business minor in a different department might be a wise choice for a budding performer.

A **Concentration,** or **Emphasis**, on the other hand, is a specialized field of study within the major you have chosen. Your major will have certain required foundation courses to complete, but then you can concentrate on one specific area of study within that broad field. For example, a Business Major might do a concentration in Sports Business or in Entrepreneurship, and would study within the same department with perhaps just a few electives from another department to individualize their degree.

University of Oregon Basic Statistics

Undergraduate Enrollment	Freshman Class Enrollment	Institution Total Enrollment	Female/Male Student Ratio	Female/Male Faculty Ratio	Student/ Faculty Ratio
18,602	4,589	22,257	55.4/44.6	46.7/53.3	18/1
# of 1st Year Applications	**# of 1st Year Women Admitted**	**# of 1st Year Men Admitted**	**# of Transfer Students Admitted**	**Overall Yield**	**% of Out-of-State Students**
31,558	17,554	11,929	2,124	16.3%	43%
% Students Living in Campus After 1st Year	**Fraternity/ Sorority Participation**	**% Students Receiving Need-based Aid**	**1st Year Students Retention Rate**	**% Classes Under 30**	**% Caucasian/ White Faculty**
27%	13%/16%	72%	87.2%	63.4%	72,2%
# Caucasian / White Students	**# Hispanic / Latinx Students**	**# Asian Students**	**# Black Students**	**# American Indian/ Alaskan, Hawaiian /Native Pacific Islander**	**# International Students**
13,585	3,126	1,468	570	98	1,073
In-State Tuition and Fees	**Room and Board Average**	**Out-of-State Tuition and Fees**	**Honors Program Cost**	**Honors Program Scholarship**	**Athletic Division**
$15,054	$14,640	$41,700	Yes, varies	varies	NCAA Div. I

Notes:

In Focus: Environmental Sciences, Ecology, and Outdoor Recreation

Attending college anywhere in the Pacific Northwest means being located in a uniquely rich and varied natural environment where Outdoor Recreation programs abound and many seasonal opportunities for outdoor adventures with other students are offered.

If you are interested in exploring Outdoor Leadership as career, several of our PNW colleges and universities offer impressive four year degrees in leadership and management of outdoor recreation and adventure programs with ample opportunities for experiential field work.

If your interest is more on scientific research focused on environment and ecology, then the Pacific Northwest offers unmatched opportunity.

You can be involved with some of the world's leading environmental and ecological research programs, including environmental health, ecosystem management, sustainability, and the impacts of climate change.

You will also have access to numerous specializations within these critical fields of study and ample opportunities for research in the natural laboratory that is the Pacific Northwest.

Idaho

The University of Idaho

UI offers nine majors in their **College of Natural Resources**. The **Environmental Science** program is unusual in that it crosses several disciplines and focuses on a whole systems approach to natural and human dimensions of environmental science. Field activities can be drawn from other departments and the program requires an individual senior capstone project.

University of Idaho's highly ranked B. S. in Recreation, Sport, and Tourism Management is a hands-on experiential program. It makes full use of nearby mountains and rivers as well as campus training facilities and focuses on developing strong people skills. RSTM majors are required to have a minor, or area of emphasis, based on their individual career goals.

Alaska

U Alaska Southeast

UAS offers an unusual **Bachelor of Liberal Arts in Outdoor and Adventure Studies** in which classes take place both on campus and in the Alaskan wilderness. Liberal arts courses focus on a student-designed portfolio of humanities courses along with a wide range of courses such as Glaciation, Swift Water Rescue, Environmental Sociology, and Outdoor Leadership.

The **UAS Program on the Environment** offers three degree options; Environmental Science B.S., Environmental Resources B.S, and Environmental Studies B.A. Entering students start as one cohort, however, and study interconnected foundational courses together before choosing their individual specializations.

Fresh Water Field Study

U Alaska at Fairbanks

UAF is the leading research institution in the circumpolar North. The extended campus includes an **Agriculture and Forestry Experiment Station, Forest Soils Lab,** a **Botanical Garden,** a **Reindeer Research Program,** the 311 acre **Fairbanks Experimental Farm,** and the **Alaska Volcano Observatory.**

UAF's Interdisciplinary Natural Resources and Environment B.S degree offers not only a deep dive into the environmental sciences, but also covers topics such as economics, policy, public lands law, and resource management, along with experiential field courses.

California

Cal Poly Humboldt

Humboldt offers three Environment focused Majors; Environmental Resources Engineering, Environmental Science and Management, and an innovative and interdisciplinary Environmental Studies B.A. degree, plus several certificates in environmental specialties, and Minors in Environmental Education and Interpretation, Env Ethics, and Env Policy, and even a minor in Scientific Diving. The **Environmental Engineering** program is one of the oldest and largest in the U.S. and focuses on water quality, water resources, and energy sources.

The University's proximity to marine and coastal environments invites research at the highest levels and supports numerous research collaborations with federal programs, nonprofit organizations, and other universities. Much of this work is headquartered at the **Humboldt Marine and Coastal Sciences Institute**. The Institute supports undergraduate research projects with grants.

Marine Science Study

The **Techiner Marine Lab** is an academic support facility of the university and the university owns the **R/V Coral Sea**, a very large and well equipped ocean-going research vessel dedicated to undergraduate education and marine research.

British Columbia

The University of British Columbia's Okanagan campus

UBCO supports a number of outstanding research facilities for environmental study including the **Fipke Lab for Trace Element Research,** the **Okanagan Institute for Biodiversity**, the **Resilience and Ecosystem Services**, the **Complex Environment Systems Lab**, a **PALEO Lab** and a **Structural Geology and Tectonic Research Group**. These enrich the **Earth and Environmental Science B.S degree** program and provide undergrad research opportunities for students. A **Freshwater Science program** focused on inland aquatic ecosystems makes use of the spectacular 84 mile long and 2 mile deep Okanagon Lake minutes from the campus.

Outdoor Recreation Leadership

Montana

Montana State University

Montana State's **Outdoor Adventure Leadership** program is focused on educational and leadership theory and practice as well as technical skills in outdoor travel and adventure. As a program of the Department of Health and Human Performance there is significant emphasis on therapeutic aspects of outdoor recreation programs and the need to transfer the learning from activity-based experiences to the daily lives and challenges of the participants.

MSU's interdisciplinary **Environmental Studies** program is solidly career oriented. Students choosing this major select a specific career track. This can be Environmental Studies with skills in Geographical Information Systems, Environmental Advocacy, Environmental Management and Policy, and/or Environmental Studies with skills in Eco-spatial Analyses track.

Students are encouraged to engage in research and must do a career-relevant internship. Experiential learning and community collaboration opportunities are built into the program.

Salish Kootenai College

SKU offers both Associate and Bachelor's degrees in **Forestry Management, Wildland Fire Management, Hydrology,** and **Wildlife and Fisheries**. These programs incorporate field studies and hands-on research in the wildlife-rich natural environments of the almost 200 sq mile **Flathead Reservation** and its great lake and river environs, south of Glacier National Park.

A major focus of SKU is on culturally centered STEM research and training, and the institution receives support in this effort from the National Science Foundation and other grants.

Tribal College Student Summer Research Institute at MSU

Washington

Western Washington University

WWU's **College of the Environment** is a premier pro-active program with an integrative approach to its eleven degree options offered in Environmental Science, Environmental Studies, and Urban and Environmental Planning and Policy, each of which offers several concentrations from which to choose.

Combined BA/BAE degrees in Business and Sustainability, Environmental Journalism, Economics, Geography, and Education and many interesting minors and certificates make this college's program both notable and uniquely flexible.

Students in this program can also design their own major/emphasis if they need something not currently offered. The campus houses six prominent Environmental Research Institutes and program facilities include a community forest, multiple laboratories, and the **Shannon Point Marine Center**. Students are also encouraged to study abroad in **International Environmental** field study programs and faculty-led **Global Learning** programs.

Oregon

Oregon State University

OSU offers Climate Science, Environmental Sciences, Ocean Science, and Geology and Geography majors within its vibrant **College of Earth, Ocean, and Atmospheric Sciences**. OSU's major analytical facilities support the **Cascadia Coastline Peoples Hazard Research Hub**, the **Coastal Imaging Lab**, the **Climate Change Research Institute**, an **Ocean Observatories Initiative** and many other research groups.

OSU's Cascades Campus offers a **Tourism, Recreation, and Adventure Leadership Education degree (TRAL)** with expedition courses on both land and water.

Southern Oregon University

SOU's **Outdoor Adventure Leadership** program offers either a B.A. or B.S degree path. The program requires students to complete an intensive 35 day program in the field during a challenging **Spring Immersion** experience. Students are given the opportunity to participate in extended international backpacking expeditions each summer to places like Nepal and Ecuador and earn multiple certifications.

Environmental Research Expedition Abroad

The B.S degree in **Environmental Science and Policy** balances social, political, biological, and earth systems sciences. It gives academic credits for internship and practicum work experiences and offers a wide range of electives that allow students a good bit of freedom in designing their own program.

Oregon Institute of Technology

Klamath Falls, Oregon / www.oit.edu

The academic emphasis at OIT is on career readiness, professional, technical, and engineering fields, and the applied sciences, especially those relating to health. The OIT job placement record is outstanding.

Location

Klamath Falls, elevation 4,094ft., is situated on the southeastern shore of a large lake just twenty-five miles north of the California-Oregon border. The small city is famous for having a system that uses geothermal power to heat homes and commercial buildings, sidewalks, and roads.

The city is on the **Pacific Flyway** for migrating waterfowl attracted by the region's abundant lakes and rivers and holds an annual **Winter Wings Festival** every February that attracts bird lovers from around the world.

Crater Lake National Park and the **Mountain Lakes Wilderness** area are nearby, as is access to outdoor activities of every kind.

The area has a high desert climate with dry summers and light winter snow, and 300 days of sunshine. Klamath Falls is served by Amtrak rail. The regional airport is 1.5 hrs. west at Medford.

Community

OIT and the Klamath Falls community's nonprofit organizations, clinics, government agencies, and businesses have close and historic bonds. These are strengthened by the research and volunteer work the students and faculty do with these organizations as part of the institute's experiential education and hands-on research educational ethic.

Students comment about the friendliness of other students and the caring staff and describe a serious sense of purpose among students here.

The student-run **College Union** serves as the center for campus activities and daily life services. Its stated mission is to create a campus community atmosphere of welcome, inclusion, engagement, and individual self-development. It also provides a forum for sharing students' ideas, interests, talents, and concerns.

The campus is adjacent to the **Sky Lakes Medical Center,** an internationally accredited acute care teaching hospital. The large complex of medical offices and clinics clustered around the Center offers a multitude of opportunities for students to receive hands-on training and experience in their chosen field.

Academics

As Oregon's only polytechnic university, the academic emphasis at OIT is on professional, technical, and engineering fields and the applied sciences, especially those relating to health. There are 47 majors and degrees offered. Engineering and Engineering Tech students account for 33% of bachelor's degrees, while 46% of degrees are gained in health professions and related fields. Most classes are under 30 students.

OIT focuses on project-based, hands-on learning, development of cross disciplinary skills and applied research. OIT offers BS degrees in Science and in Applied Science including Civil, Electrical, Renewable Energy and Mechanical Engineering and related technical programs. OIT's **Nuclear Medicine and Molecular Imaging Technology** BS degree is one of seven medical technology B.S. degree programs responding to increased demand for highly trained technical staff in hospitals and research clinics.

Dow Center for Health Professions offers state of the art medical tech training facilities. The Biology–Health Science and Nursing programs prepare students for medical, dentistry, pharmacy, nursing, veterinary, and other medical professions. The **Applied Psychology** program provides a flexible skill-based core program for students pursuing related careers. Many students add minors to their programs to augment their skills and knowledge base and there are options for dual majors and 4+1 graduate degrees.

OIT developed the nation's first bachelor level program in **Population Health Management.** This program offers a foundation in medical sociology in an interdisciplinary curriculum with applied courses. It is coordinated with the **Population Health Management Research Center**, which provides research and experiential learning opportunities for students.

OIT's entrepreneurial student/faculty research teams work on multiple projects in conjunction with businesses and government entities. OIT manages the **Oregon Renewable Energy** and **Geo-Heat Centers**, both of which offer students valuable experience as lab and research assistants. The **Oregon Manufacturing Innovation Center** provides several scholarships and internship opportunities for OIT students.

Other research relationships include the **Nanoscience and Micro Technologies Institute**, the **National Energy Technology Laboratory**, **KersTech Vehicle Systems**, a Support Network for **Research and Innovation in Solar Energy**, and businesses such as **Arcimoto, Inc.**, an electric vehicle manufacturer. OIT seniors produce Senior Projects, many of which are supported by industry partners.

Recreational Activities and Residential Life

OIT athletes compete in 6 men's and 7 women's NAIA intercollegiate sports in the Cascade Collegiate Conference. The athletic department's Tech-Fit program is open to all students, and the spacious new **TechRec Center** has a multipurpose sports court and a full range of cardio and weight equipment. The popular **Outdoor Program** offers activities in mountain and winter sports, river and sea expeditions, hot springs, camping, biking, and even skydiving experiences, and low cost equipment rentals.

Student-led programs include everything from **Oregon Tech Racing Formula SAE Club** and the **Autonomous Unmanned Vehicle Systems** and **Intelligent Robotics** team to **Blacksmithing** and **Beekeeping**, as well as identity and professions-based organizations such as the **Society of Women Engineers**.

OIT students run the radio station and college newspaper, can join dance, theater, a pep band, and the **Treehouse**, a diversity and inclusion support program.

Housing is available in two units, the three-story Residence Hall, which offers double and single rooms, and a suite style apartment building called Sustainable Village. About 65% of first year students choose to begin with residential housing, but 83%of undergrads eventually find housing off campus.

Financial Aid

The Institute offers numerous scholarships for both in state and out of state students, most based on merit or participation on academic teams and/or athletic talent, leadership, diversity, and other criteria. Some scholarships are specifically for local students. OIT is a **WUE** school as well.

Study Away

OIT has an exchange agreement with Metropolia University in Helsinki, Finland, for various tech degrees. OIT works exclusively with **IE3Global**, an organization of Oregon State University, in providing study away programs and full-time international internships for Oregon students.

IE3Global

IE3Global is a program headquartered at Oregon State University. It has over fifty years of experience offering study abroad and exchange opportunities, and more than two decades of success with international internships and experimental learning programs.

The IE3Global organization has university and private college partners throughout the northwest. Qualified students at these partner institutions who have financial needs can apply for program fee reductions, and students' financial aid packages may be used for travel and internships abroad.

IE3Global partners with over 130 businesses, organizations, and agencies worldwide where students can have full time internships. For example, four-week Clinical Health Rotations at children's health clinics in Africa, Agricultural Education in Thailand, Business or Engineering Internships in Germany, and many more options are available.

Oregon Institute of Technogy Basic Statistics

Undergraduate Enrollment	Freshman Class Enrollment	Institution Total Enrollment	Female/Male Student Ratio	Female/Male Faculty Ratio	Student/ Faculty Ratio
4,776	403	4,910	52/48	44/56	18/1
# of 1st Year Applications	**# of 1st Year Women Admitted**	**# of 1st Year Men Admitted**	**# of Transfer Students Admitted**	**Overall Yield**	**% of Out-of-State Students**
4,593	2,443	1,719	807	11%	27.2%
% Students Living in Campus After 1st Year	**Fraternity/ Sorority Participation**	**% Students Receiving Need-based Aid**	**1st Year Students Retention Rate**	**% Classes Under 30**	**% Caucasian/ White Faculty**
20.4%	n/a	37%	67.9%	65%	84%
# Caucasian / White Students	**# Hispanic / Latinx Students**	**# Asian Students**	**# Black Students**	**# American Indian/ Alaskan, Hawaiian /Native Pacific Islander**	**# International Students**
3,242	623	400	88	78	54
In-State Tuition and Fees	**Room and Board Average**	**Out-of-State Tuition and Fees**	**Honors Program Cost**	**Honors Program Scholarship**	**Athletic Division**
$11,622	$9,280	$32,516	0	varies	NCIA Div. II

Notes:

Portland State University

Portland, Oregon / www. pdx.edu

PSU attracts students who want a vibrant and progressive city experience, a wide range of academic programs to explore, and a first year seminar cohort program that encourages community building and initial student-faculty engagement.

Location

Portland, Oregon's largest city, sits at sea level on the Columbia and Willamette rivers, in the shadow of the impressive snow-capped Mount Hood. With a population of 666,000 the city serves as both a vibrant hub and a generator of innovative art, theater, music, and cultural diversity for a metro area of 2.5 million. Portland is a green city, known for its environmental sustainability practices, and for the nearly 12,000 acres of parks and open spaces that invite hikers and bikers along 157 miles of trails.

The Portland vibe is casual and laid back. You rarely see men in suits, for instance, but famous companies like Nike, Intel, Pixelworks, Columbia, and new clean technology companies located here have generated the nickname of **Silicon Forest** for the area and fueled an influx of new residents attracted by the job market.

Winters can be overcast and misty, but temperatures are generally mild all year. The city's various eclectic neighborhoods are very walkable, with great public transport in between, and there is a different coffee house around most every corner.

Community

Nearly 18,000 undergraduates are enrolled at Portland State, with 79% being Oregon residents and 52% identifying as White. Over 90% of PSU students live off campus, or commute to classes from outlying areas. The University is located just south of downtown in a 12 block area called the **University District**. The center for services, meetings, and information and support services is the **Smith Memorial Student Union.** It has a gaming room and bowling alley, several places to eat, and an art gallery.

Portland State is known for a student population with strong liberal leanings and for its support of students of diverse identities and cultures. **The Student Community Engagement Center** provides resources for finding and engaging in community based volunteer service projects, including those required in many PSU courses. The **Multicultural Student Center** supports a variety of **Cultural Resource Centers** on campus which encourage student leadership and collaboration, provide resources, sponsor events and programs, and have lounge and study spaces for members of various cultural identity groups.

Academics

PSU undergraduate academics are divided into Upper and Lower Divisions within the College of the Arts, the School of Business, the Maseeh College of Engineering and Computer Sciences, the University Honors College, the College of Liberal Arts and Sciences, the College of Urban and Public Affairs, and the Schools of Social Work and Public Health.

PSU's campus is a model of sustainability. Its motto, "Let Knowledge Serve the City" inspires not only faculty and student research, but encourages place-based experiential learning with the city serving as an extended campus and living laboratory. The innovative **University Studies (UNST)** program is required of all undergrads, except those in the Honors College, or majoring in Liberal Studies.

UNST first year students join a small group Freshman Inquiry class that builds foundational skills and introduces different modes of inquiry and tools. Students get to focus on a real world issue of interest to them (a theme of inquiry), while studying core subjects from an interdisciplinary perspective with the same cohort all year.

The University Honors College is the only **urban-focused honors college** in the nation. It offers a different approach to a college curriculum for students who have solid preparation for academic challenges. It basically serves as a small, rigorous liberal arts college within the greater university.

As Oregon's only urban-serving Research University, the emphasis is on addressing critical issues and bold action. Research Centers on campus include one for Electron Microscopy and Nanofabrication, as well as the Digital City Testbed Center, Transportation Research, Sustainable Solutions for Livable Cities, and a Homelessness Research and Action Collaborative, among many others.

Recreational Activities and Residential Living

The Campus Recreation Center offers a full range of indoor and outdoor recreation options, from a climbing center to a pool, fitness classes and equipment, outdoor trips and gear rentals, and personal training. It has accessible, adaptive, and inclusive programs as well. Intramural sports include an indoor soccer league, and many of the Rec Clubs participate in intercollegiate competition. The Portland State Vikings compete in 5 men's and 8 women's NCAA sports.

There are hundreds of student organizations at PSU, including seven Greek societies, cultural identity clubs, arts, business, pre-professional, and spiritual organizations. PSU encourages students to explore leadership opportunities in these clubs, and serve on boards and councils.

First year students who live on campus can select from six living/learning residential communities that share similar interests and are engaged in the First Year Experience, and about half of the students in each class do so. Honors College students have a choice of **Honors Community Residences**. Residents have to select a Meal Plan. The Victor's Dining Center is the main venue for meals, but there are many other small ones.

Financial Aid

Oregon residents who receive a Pell grant can have standard tuition and fees covered for four years. The University also offers **Opportunity Scholarships** to both residents and out of state applicants who are academically qualified and income-eligible. There is a Washington Border discount and **WUE**.

Study Away

At PSU it is easy to find a study away program that fulfills some of a student's major and/or minor requirements. The Academic Departments and the Education Abroad office collaborate on advising students of their options for study, internships, and research and there are myriad choices available. There are also multiple scholarships which provide financial support for these programs.

Digital City Testbed Center

The DCT Center at Portland State is engaging academic faculty and researchers at five PNW colleges and universities in collaborative interdisciplinary research projects. The Center's mission is to improve the health and safety of urban buildings and transportation systems, preserve urban trees, and increase accessibility for all, while still protecting privacy and security.

The term 'testbed' refers to a platform for experimentation of large project concepts. It is a modeling tool to study system components and interactions to gain insight into how an actual system might look like and work. The platform provides a realistic hardware-software environment in which to test individual parts of a system design, before actually building it.

This DCT project is meant to aid cities in making critical decisions about land use and informed investments of resources that will result in greener, more sustainable, and healthier cities for all, and be a model from which others can learn. A city has many built layers and complicated environments that pose a challenge to improving the health and welfare of its inhabitants. Smart cities/digital cities must draw from many, and varied, expert sources, data, and technology.

For students at these institutions, participating in ambitious research projects such as the DCT can inspire and inform. They also demonstrate the benefits of innovative and collaborative teamwork, technology, and shared commitments toward a sustainable future and equitable health outcomes. These are skills and experiences employers want to see on resumes.

Portland State University Basic Statistics

Undergraduate Enrollment	Freshman Class Enrollment	Institution Total Enrollment	Female/Male Student Ratio	Female/Male Faculty Ratio	Student/ Faculty Ratio
18,045	2,272	23,181	52/48	54/56	15/1
# of 1st Year Applications	**# of 1st Year Women Admitted**	**# of 1st Year Men Admitted**	**# of Transfer Students Admitted**	**Overall Yield**	**% of Out-of-State Students**
6,859	4,399	2,352	4,415	24%	17%
% Students Living in Campus After 1st Year	**% Fraternity/ Sorority Participation**	**% Students Receiving Need-based Aid**	**1st Year Students Retention Rate**	**% Classes Under 30**	**% Caucasian/ White Faculty**
9%	2%/5%	54%	72.2%	72%	82%
# Caucasian / White Students	**# Hispanic / Latinx Students**	**# Asian Students**	**# Black Students**	**# American Indian/ Alaskan, Hawaiian /Native Pacific Islander**	**# International Students**
8,885	3,360	1,944	759	327	574
In-State Tuition and Fees	**Room and Board Average**	**Out-of-State Tuition and Fees**	**Honors Program Cost**	**Honors Program Scholarship**	**Athletic Division**
$10,386	$11.853	$29,286	$350	varies	NCAA Div. I

Notes:

Southern Oregon University

Ashland, Oregon / www. sou.edu

Southern Oregon U attracts students to its outstanding fine and performing arts programs, innovative departments of Communications, and Emerging Data and Media Arts, and other professional career pathways.

Location

Ashland is located in the Rogue Valley of southern Oregon, just north of the California border. The small city is well-known for its arts and music culture, and entrepreneurial businesses.

Ashland is home of the internationally acclaimed **Oregon Shakespeare Festival's** professional repertory theater. The company produces contemporary dramatic works and musicals, as well as Shakespearean plays, in three theaters, over a ten month season, bringing many thousands of theater lovers to the city each year.

The Rogue Valley region is known for its prize winning vineyards and outdoor recreation options in the surrounding Cascade and Siskiyou mountain ranges, and in the river valleys. Interesting restaurants, shops, pubs, shops, and coffee houses fill the historic downtown. The busy regional airport just twenty minutes north at Medford is served by multiple airlines.

Weather is warm and dry in summer months, and relatively mild in winter, with occasional smoke from forest fires.

Community

SOU is known as an inclusive and welcoming community committed to sustainability and career-focused academic offerings. Student comments refer to the campus and community as full of kind and accepting people and report that professors seem enthusiastic about their subjects and responsive to student needs.

A first year **Bridge Program** experience supports social, emotional, and academic strengths and welcomes underrepresented students. A four-day **Raider Wilderness Experience** introduces new students to the Southern Oregon outdoors and fosters new friendships among participants. The **Honors** program attracts students who want not only a rigorous cohort learning experience but also one that focuses on community interaction and service.

The **Associated Students of SOU** organization serves as the student government. Its leaders fight for issues that matter to students and are committed to community building through social organizing, legislative advocacy, and voter registration. **Stevenson Union** is the community hub for community activities and services.

Academics

The most popular majors at SOU include those in the Business fields and in the Visual and Performing Arts, followed by Psychology, Education, and Parks and Recreation. A strong and flexible **Interdisciplinary Studies** program allows students to draw from three or four departments in support of their individual interests.

An innovative **Emerging Media/Digital Arts** program offers either a B.A or B.S degree pathway that develops technical skills and creative professional design studio competencies for success in a wide range of media careers. SOU's **Accelerated Baccalaureate Degree** program is possible for students entering with advanced high school coursework and can save as much as a year of tuition costs.

Although the student to faculty ratio at SOU is 20:1, most classes have fewer than thirty students. Psychology students can choose an emphasis on experimental, clinical, counseling, development, or organization psychology to fit their career plans and internships, and practicums are encouraged to gain hands-on experience. The **Cognition and Evolutionary Psychology Research** lab offers undergraduate research opportunities.

Digital Cinema is a major for creative visual storytellers and offers experiential classes with on-set opportunities that build professional production skills. The comprehensive **Music Department** curriculum begins with a core program in theory, aural skills, history, and solo and ensemble performance experience. From there, the students can forge their own path into a music-related career of their choice with professional guidance from an exceptional music faculty.

SOU's well-regarded Theater program benefits from its proximity to the Oregon Shakespeare Festival, and its professional actors, designers, and directors who serve as adjunct faculty and guest artists. Qualified students find ample opportunity for internships and apprenticeships not only at OSF but with a variety of other professional and semi-professional community theater companies in the area. The University's student productions also meet high standards and draw enthusiastic audiences.

Recreational Activities and Residential Living

The **Student Recreation Center** is a new 50,000 sq. ft. facility catering to all fitness and exercise needs, and serves Intramurals and Sport Clubs for all skills levels. The fifty year old **Outdoor Program** offers a variety of adventure trips and all the gear needed, as well as an indoor climbing wall for practice. Whitewater rafting is popular and miles of challenging mountain biking trails snake through the forests above the campus. The Outdoor program even produces its own newsletter to keep students informed of upcoming options and stories. Varsity athletes compete in seven men's and nine women's sports in the NAIA in the Frontier Conference.

SOU Presence offers connections to the sixty or more clubs and leadership opportunities available on campus. These include unique ones such as the Medieval Arts club and a Pollinator Club, activist groups such as the Society for Advancement of Chicano/Hispanics and Native Americans in Science, and the **Social Justice and Equity Center** and many more.

Four residence halls include the new **Raider Village** complex, and an LBGTQIA+ themed hall. McLoughlin Hall has a suite design and kitchenettes and Madrone Hall for returning students has single bedroom suites with full kitchens. There is also multicultural-themed housing and a variety of meal plans.

Financial Aid

SOU has a reciprocal **North State Promise** agreement with three northern California community colleges and five northern California county high schools, which invites their students to attend at in-state tuition rate.

In addition to the **WUE** reduced tuition option, SOU offers a number of merit based scholarships for both in state and out of state students. The **Honors College** students also receive a scholarship, but pay a small extra fee for each honors course credit.

Study Away

The **Office of International Programs** is SOU's resource for study abroad programs or programs in other states and with other North American partners through the **National Student Exchange.**

Accelerated Degrees

With an accelerated degree program a student can reduce higher education time by at least one year, at substantial cost savings. These programs are intensive, and require commitment and persistence.

Many of the heavily advertised Accelerated B.A. programs are online programs which can vary significantly in quality and design. However, the one offered by SOU is in-person. AccBacc works best if the student has made a firm decision about the major they want, as there is not enough time in the program for exploration.

AccBacc students at SOU carry a normal course load of 16 credits per term, but the number of general education and elective credits courses are reduced. Applicants must meet GPA and other academic qualifications in order to do an AccBacc degree program.

SOU offers AccBacc in 18 different majors, and careful planning is necessary, as well as maintenance of normal progress. It is also possible to complete a Minor in SOU's AccBacc program.

Southern Oregon University Basic Statistics

Undergraduate Enrollment	Freshman Class Enrollment	Institution Total Enrollment	Female/Male Student Ratio	Female/Male Faculty Ratio	Student/ Faculty Ratio
3,124	706	5,089	61/39	53.5/46.5	20/1
# of 1st Year Applications	**# of 1st Year Women Admitted**	**# of 1st Year Men Admitted**	**# of Transfer Students Admitted**	**Overall Yield**	**% of Out-of-State Students**
1,870	1,065	681	572	40%	28.2%
% Students Living in Campus After 1st Year	**% Fraternity/ Sorority Participation**	**% Students Receiving Need-based Aid**	**1st Year Students Retention Rate**	**% Classes Under 30**	**% Caucasian/ White Faculty**
22%	0%	69.9%	65.3%	85.4%	81.7%
# Caucasian / White Students	**# Hispanic / Latinx Students**	**# Asian Students**	**# Black Students**	**# American Indian/ Alaskan, Hawaiian /Native Pacific Islander**	**# International Students**
2,896	608	165	75	148	67
In-State Tuition and Fees	**Room and Board Average**	**Out-of-State Tuition and Fees**	**Honors Program Cost**	**Honors Program Scholarship**	**Athletic Division**
$9,357	$14,250	$23,613	$25 per honors credit hour	varies	NAIA Div. II

Notes:

Vancouver Island University

Nanaimo, B.C. / www.viu.ca

This regional university, in the warmest location in Canada, is noted for its focus on excellent teaching, support and encouragement of student potential, and innovative experiential and cross-cultural learning programs.

Location

Nanaimo, with a population of about 100,000, is a ferry port on the east coast of Vancouver Island, British Columbia, northwest of the capital city of Victoria and directly across the Salish Sea from Vancouver city. It sits on a coastal headland, so has a waterfront on three sides. Heavily forested **Mount Benson**, with its rugged trails and abundance of wildlife, rises behind the city. The Vancouver Island climate is quite mild compared to most of Canada, with rainy winters and warm, dry summers. It can be reached by ferry, from two locations in the Vancouver city area, and by air.

Nanaimo has a revitalized downtown core with unique shopping, dining, and entertainment options in the Arts District, the historic Old City Quarter, and the Waterfront District. There is a long **Harbour Front Walkway** and several city parks, some with waterfalls, trails, and swimmable lakes. A ten-minute ferry ride takes you to Newcastle Island, a **Provincial Marine Park** with multiple beaches and coastal trails for biking and hiking.

Community

VIU is a welcoming regional campus serving about 7,000 undergraduates, 12% of whom are Native indigenous and 11% international. The University's mission is to be an innovative teaching campus offering excellent and unique educational opportunities across multiple disciplines founded on community strengths. It promotes campus community with small class sizes that encourage faculty/student engagement, supports Aboriginal learners and connection to Aboriginal communities, and fosters global awareness.

Students report that VIU is an environmentally friendly campus with a responsive staff. Access and inclusion are particular strengths of VIU programming. The University provides students with dedicated professional counseling and advising services that support academic and personal success and has special programs for Aboriginal learners, non-traditional students, and previously fostered youth.

Academics

VIU takes a holistic approach to higher education and training and focuses on helping learners embrace their potential. Education about the experiences of Indigenous Peoples in Canada is integrated across VIU both in formal coursework and through informal opportunities for employee and student learning. The University contributes to the regional economy through student and faculty engagement in the community with research, internships, and co-op learning partnerships.

The B.A degree is promoted as the most customizable program at VIU, allowing for self-designed interdisciplinary education and training. Students may take Honours levels courses and do an Honours thesis in preparation for graduate study or choose a double major, and also minors of interest. The humanities, social sciences, and arts programs at VIU include global studies, creative writing and journalism, Studies in Women and Gender, and Digital Media, among many other options.

VIU's science and technology department offers Diplomas in 28-month technology programs, and four year Bachelor of Science degrees, with choices of Honours, majors, and minors. The STEM program offers many options, including co-op programs in computer science, a biological and lab-based psychology curriculum, a full range of rigorous mathematics courses, and Geoscience, Chemistry, and Biology, and multiple minors. All STEM degrees focus on experiential learning in small classes and labs.

Health profession training includes a B.S. in Nursing and diplomas and certifications in multiple health assistant training programs. An impressive number of diplomas and certificates are offered in multiple trades and technology fields as well, including Information Technology and Applied Systems, and in several apprenticeship and co-op programs from Forest Harvesting Practices to Marine and Motorcycle Mechanical Technician training to an Aboriginal Construction apprenticeship program.

Recreational Activities and Residential Life

VIU's Student Union is a powerful voice for student issues and social action, and functions as a student activities and events leader and promoter. It works with the **Office of Student Advocacy** to resolve disputes and responds to student appeals and complaints. Student empowerment, collective action, and meaningful change are among the Union's priorities. The **Student Union Pub** hosts music and fun gatherings and there are many student clubs and organizations.

Campus recreation includes fitness classes, intramurals, and health and wellness programs. Multiple basketball, volleyball, and badminton courts, plus dance and fitness classes are available at the VIU gymnasium. The **Outdoors Recreation** program takes advantage of the University's location by providing a full range of water sports, serious hiking and biking, and overnight camping and expeditions. Competitive Intramural leagues feature volleyball, basketball, and indoor soccer. Varsity athletes compete in golf, baseball, soccer, volleyball, basketball, and badminton, and have championship records in several sports.

Student housing is available for 500 students in ten buildings on campus, ranging from traditional dorms to townhouses and apartments. First year students get priority if they apply by the deadline. A cafeteria managed by the professional culinary program offers plenty of options including Contemporary and French cuisine. Nanaimo city offers affordable housing off campus and a HomeStay program is available.

Financial Aid

Canadian students have several options for financial aid, including government grants for Canadian students. U.S. students can use Federal Education loans at Canadian universities, but not Pell grants. U.S. students with a valid study permit may work for pay for up to twenty hours per week. A limited number of merit scholarships are offered to international students.

Study Away

Vancouver Island University's VIU Education Abroad program offers exchange programs with partner universities in thirteen countries, including the **UARTIC Network**. Several departments also include international travel and study options in specific courses.

Study Abroad Programs

Study Abroad offices can be found at most colleges and universities and these vary substantially in what services and opportunities they offer. The advantages of study abroad include gaining new and diverse perspectives and broadening knowledge and understanding of the world. It gives students experience in global travel, self-sufficiency, and independence and exposes them to different social and cultural norms. These experiences help prepare them for working in global industries and international organizations.

Students can choose a study abroad program that complements their major or minor and gives them a deeper understanding of their subject and an opportunity for research. Many institutions offer study abroad financial aid grants and scholarships to students who qualify.

Universities often team up to offer their students wider international study options. For instance VIU has a partnership with Toronto Metropolitan University's Florence, Italy program. This offers an inclusive three course package that includes classroom time and on-site study at museums, galleries and artistic and cultural sites, plus study tours to other cities and historic sites and housing. Other study abroad programs may offer homestays, opportunities for volunteer service, and full language immersion. International internships are also gaining popularity.

Vancouver Island University Basic Statistics

Undergraduate Enrollment	Freshman Class Enrollment	Institution Total Enrollment	Female/Male Student Ratio	Female/Male Faculty Ratio	Student/ Faculty Ratio
7,137	4,348	12,724	60/40	--	--
# of 1st Year Applications	**# of 1st Year Women Admitted**	**# of 1st Year Men Admitted**	**# of Transfer Students Admitted**	**Overall Yield**	**% of Out-of-State Students**
8,011	--	--	--	--	11%
% Students Living in Campus Housing	**% Fraternity/ Sorority Participation**	**% Students Receiving Need-based Aid**	**1st Year Students Retention Rate**	**% Classes Under 30**	**% Caucasian/ White Faculty**
4.5%	n/a	--	--	Max class Size of 34	--
# Caucasian / White Students	**# Hispanic / Latinx Students**	**# Asian Students**	**# Black Students**	**# Native Canadian or Pacific Islanders**	**# International Students**
--	--	--	--	1,494	1,412
In-Country Tuition and Fees	**Room and Board Average**	**International Tuition and Fees**	**Honors Program Cost**	**Honors Program Scholarship**	**Athletic Division**
$6,750 CAD	Varies/Homestay Program Available	$19,300 CAD	--	--	CCAA-Canadian Collegiate Athletic Assn.

Notes:

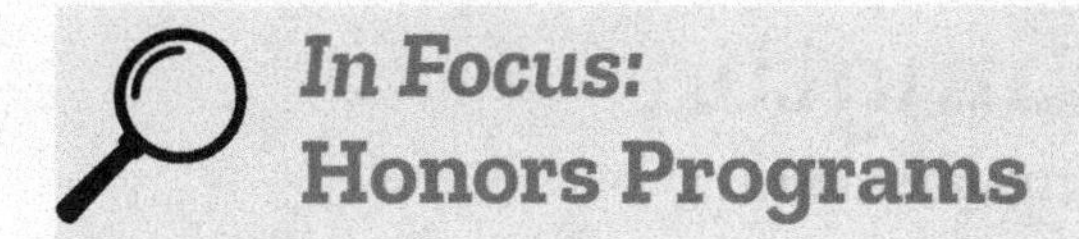

In Focus: Honors Programs

The term Honors can be confusing so here is some clarification.

Purpose

Among the larger public universities, Honors programs began to be developed to compete with prestigious private colleges for the purpose of attracting academically outstanding students who prefer the small seminar type classes, strong faculty-student interaction, support, and flexibility offered by most private liberal arts colleges.

By providing an honors program with the same type of innovative small classes taught by distinguished faculty, many public universities compete very successfully for these high achieving students.

Honors Programs

These programs take different forms at different institutions, although all offer certain advantages to students who are enrolled in them, and most engage students throughout their undergraduate years.

Honors Colleges

The most comprehensive honors programs are designated as Honors Colleges and often have special housing and classroom amenities, designated staff, and other nice perks, in addition to a special curriculum and small classes.

Advantages

✔ Honors scholarships are often offered by public institutions, and added to their lower tuition, these can be an additional incentive to enroll there.

✔ Specialized small seminar courses replace core curriculum in part or entirely with more rigorous and/or specialized curricula open only to honors college students and taught by outstanding faculty. Greater opportunity for undergraduate research, advanced studies, study abroad, conferences, etc.

✔ Designated meeting and study spaces on campus for Honors students, designated classrooms and/or special housing and housing amenities and activities that encourage close knit community building among honors students.

✔ Priority course registration may be available for honors students to design a class schedule that best suits their needs.

Acceptance to an Honors College

Applicants to Honors programs have to meet certain qualifications. These may include a certain GPA score and other indication of high academic, leadership, or creative potential.

Most also require a separate application which may include essays or short answer questions and additional recommendations.

Graduating with Honors

To receive a degree with honors recognizes that you have done academic work as an undergraduate which is of higher caliber than other graduates in your class. You will have that distinction noted on your diploma and can use it on your resume.

Many colleges will use the terms cum laude (with praise), magna cum laude, (with great praise), and summa cum laude (with highest praise), to indicate different levels of academic achievement.

You do not necessarily have to have been enrolled in an Honors Program to attain an Honors distinction. It can also reflect individual excellence in your major field, or indicate that your overall undergraduate record puts you at, or near the top, of your entire graduating class.

Cautions

Some Honors programs are better than others. Dig deep to understand exactly what you get. How many Honors courses are there to choose from? Do you still need to take some large lecture core courses, or does your Honors program cover all core requirements?

Can you balance a STEM major, labs, and extracurriculars, with the demands of the honors program? What GPA do you need to maintain your Honors scholarship?

Some public universities charge students an extra fee for the privilege of participating in the Honors College or program, even if they award them a scholarship. This can make an unexpected dent in your Honors Scholarship. Always ask so you will know what that will mean to your overall tuition and fees charges.

University of Washington

Seattle, Washington / www.washington.edu

One of the nation's most prestigious public research universities, UW is known for its extensive number of interdisciplinary Research Centers and Institutes. It is also a Sea Grant and NASA Space Grant institution.

Location

An oceanic port situated on a hilly isthmus between Puget Sound and Lake Washington, Seattle is the largest city in the Pacific Northwest. The metro area is one of the fastest growing in the U.S., and home to major companies such as Boeing, Microsoft, and Amazon, and an ever expanding list of other tech companies.

The city is gradually growing in diversity and is a notable hub for global health organizations. Seattle is also a regional center for the visual and performing arts and an historic incubator of successful popular musical groups. The climate is Mediterranean with cool, wet winters and mild dry summers.

Because so many city residents regularly engage in outdoor recreation, from walking and cycling to the full range of water and mountain sports readily available, the city has earned the title of "fittest city." Seattle is also famous for its many artisan coffeehouses, its more than a hundred theater companies, and equal number of art galleries. Seattle's street cars and light rail make getting around the city relatively easy. Sea-Tac International airport serves both the Seattle metro area and the nearby city of Tacoma.

Community

Thanks to Seattle's bountiful rain, the UW campus is lush, green, and beautiful, especially in the springtime. It is also well situated for easy access to downtown.

Students comment on the friendliness of people and that there are abundant resources for engagement in community life, but that accessing these requires initiative and self-advocacy. Being proactive is a must in this very large university of 36,206 undergraduates and 16,233 graduate students; otherwise, it is easy to feel lost in the crowd.

The campus can seem almost like a city unto itself. Still, there are many welcoming student-led and organized clubs to join that allow students to make connections, find friends and discover a comfortable and fun place within the larger community. UW provides a space for all students to be included, challenged, and supported in their educational journey. CLUE tutoring and Academic Success Coaching are available in-person and virtually.

Academics

UW is internationally recognized for its STEM departments and research. Courses are very rigorous, and several popular majors are capacity constrained, so competition for admittance to those majors is extremely tough. Those considering UW should be aware that they could spend two years here and still not get into the major of their choice, unless directly admitted freshman year. Unfortunately not all UW programs have a **Direct to Major** option. This is not an academic environment that easily accommodates students who come with only vague ideas about what to major in and expect to take their time exploring various career paths.

Students see the larger class sizes and challenging prerequisite coursework for those ultra-competitive majors as a way for the University to weed out all but the most dedicated and high achieving students. Nonetheless, the faculty consists of excellent professors, many renowned in their fields and good at facilitating learning. UW is home to a huge number of research centers covering a wide range of fields of study, including many that are health or natural environment-related.

Ambitious and focused students will find ample support as they dig into their upper level courses and access the University's abundant resources and opportunities. The largest number of undergraduate degrees are awarded in the social sciences, biological and life sciences, and engineering fields, followed by computer and information sciences and business programs. The **Honors Program** offers interdisciplinary and college honors options in small classes for 1300+ selected students.

Recreational Activities and Residential Living

Although first year students are not required to live on campus, about 71% do choose to as a way to transition into college life, and about a third of students choose UW housing beyond first year. Thirteen residence halls are available, many with Living/ Learning Communities such as the Pre-health sciences LLC, Engineering LLC, Arts LLC, etc. Most halls have access either to nearby amenities, or ones right on site, such as maker spaces, game rooms, and creative spaces. Some even have a fitness center, dining service, and a market. Gender inclusivity is offered in most halls. Students report that dorms are nice inside, but suggest checking out the city neighborhoods in which they are located, as some locations are deemed safer than others. Multiple levels of meal plans are offered to fit students' varied budgets and needs.

The **Husky Union Building** houses the **Student Activities Office**, the **Q Center**, study areas, networking, and resources for Registered Student Organizations (RSOs), which number an astounding 864. Included in this large list of student organizations are seventy fraternities and sororities in which about 4700 students participate. Greek societies' programs, activities, and community service projects make contributions to community life at the University, while also providing a lively party scene.

Recreational options include numerous **Rec Clubs**, some of which compete in a sport or martial art. The **IMA** building is the main rec center on campus for personal fitness and intramural sports. A comprehensive range of recreational activities on and off campus is available, and many of these access nearby waterfronts, mountains, and beaches. UW varsity athletes compete in 21 sports at the NCAA Division I level, in the North Division of the Pac-12.

Financial Aid

UW is unfortunately not a WUE participant university, but its stellar academic reputation still draws many out of state students. No state grants are offered to out of state students, but some scholarships such as the **Purple and Gold, UW Honors**, and many academic department scholarships are open to out of state students.

Study Away

UW provides in depth advising on multiple study abroad programs and costs. The unique **Bonderman Fellowship** funds a small number of students each year for eight months of independent travel and exploration.

The NASA Space Grant

The NASA Space Grant program supports a national network of colleges and universities working on expanding opportunities for Americans to understand and participate in NASA's aeronautics and space projects. It helps underwrite and enhance science and engineering education, research, and public outreach efforts.

The national network includes over 850 affiliates from universities, colleges, industry, museums, science centers, and state and local agencies that form a Consortium coordinated by a state research university.

The University of Alaska Fairbanks, University of Washington, Montana State University, University of Idaho, and Oregon State University are each NASA Grant Consortia Leaders in their respective states.

These Consortia fund curriculum enhancement and faculty development, along with fellowships and scholarships for students pursuing careers in science, mathematics, engineering, or technology (STEM).

Member colleges and universities also administer pre-college and public service education projects in their states. Many Consortia fund well-paying summer research positions for students.

University of Washington Basic Statistics

Undergraduate Enrollment	Freshman Class Enrollment	Institution Total Enrollment	Female/Male Student Ratio	Female/Male Faculty Ratio	Student/ Faculty Ratio
36,206	7,552	52,439	56/44	48/52	21/1

# of 1st Year Applications	# of 1st Year Women Admitted	# of 1st Year Men Admitted	# of Transfer Students Admitted	Overall Yield	% of Out-of-State Students
48,840	16,290	9,831	2,299	28%	29%

% Students Living in Campus After 1st Year	% Fraternity/ Sorority Participation	% Students Receiving Need-based Aid	1st Year Students Retention Rate	% Classes Under 30	% Caucasian/ White Faculty
31%	13%/12%	38%	92.98%	55%	77%

# Caucasian / White Students	# Hispanic / Latinx Students	# Asian Students	# Black Students	# American Indian/ Alaskan, Hawaiian /Native Pacific Islander	# International Students
11,321	2,969	8,507	1,086	236	4409

In-State Tuition and Fees	Room and Board Average	Out-of-State Tuition and Fees	Honors Program Cost	Honors Program Scholarship	Athletic Division
$12,076	$14,871	$39,906	0	various	NAIA Div. II Pac-12

Notes:

Western Washington University

Bellingham, Washington / www. wwu.edu

In one of the most scenic areas of the Pacific Northwest, and very near the Canadian border, WWU offers distinctive interdisciplinary programs and experiential research opportunities to a diverse and pro-active student and faculty community.

Location

Bellingham is an eco-conscious, outdoorsy community of nearly 90,000 situated on a protected bay between the Pacific coast and the Cascade Mountain range of northwest Washington. It is just 21 miles south of the Canadian border. A walkable downtown has shops, restaurants, and art galleries to explore, and night-life. Being a port city, it has a very active waterfront and boardwalk. You can take a ferry to Alaska, roam the many inlets and beaches, or hike and ski on Mt. Baker, elev. 10,786ft., in the **Mt.Baker –Snoqualmie National Forest**. A public bus system serves the city and surrounding neighborhoods, and walking trails link the more than a dozen city parks, including the 241 acre **Whatcom Falls Park**, with its four sets of waterfalls.

There are about 200 sunny days per year, rainy springs, but not much snow. Temperatures are cool in winter and warm, but not hot in summer. Four airlines serve the international airport in Bellingham and Amtrak connects to Seattle and Vancouver, B.C., and beyond.

Community

The WWU campus sits on a hill at the south end of the city adjacent to a 180 acre arboretum and nature park and has a positive relationship with the city. It provides many programs that support the area community, residents, and businesses. WWU includes about 12,500 full time and 1500 part time undergraduates.

The Office of Civic Engagement (OCE) provides resources, services, and support to ensure student representation in decisions that impact students at the university, local, state, and federal levels. The AS Review is a pro-active, student-run news organization that keeps the community informed of events and issues, and serves as a forum for sharing information and ideas.

Fairhaven College and the **Honors College** offer smaller community living options within the larger university and more flexible curricular requirements. **Viking Launch** gives first year students a week-long intensive prep program to ease them into the college community and academic life

Academics

WWU academics are grouped into seven divisions called Colleges. These include the colleges of Business and Economics, Fine and Performing Arts, Science and Engineering, Humanities and Social Sciences, the College of the Environment, the Woodring College of Education, and the Fairhaven College of Interdisciplinary Studies. The Honors College serves students of all disciplines.

Students comment on the University's open and friendly character, and its sense of connection with other students and faculty. Class sizes in the general education courses can be as large as 50-75 students, but once in your major courses they are usually well under thirty. The Hacherl Research and Writing Studio provides assistance to students across all subjects.

The University has many specialized institutes and centers that offer undergraduate research and interdisciplinary exploration, and some are uniquely representative of the university's border and coastal location. These include the **Center for Canadian-American Studies,** the **Border Policy Research Institute,** the **Salish Sea Institute, SEA Discovery Center,** and **Marine and Coastal Science.**

Fairhaven College offers seminar type courses in place of those large general education classes, as does the Honors College. Nonetheless, students say that most professors, even in the larger classes, are accessible to, and supportive of, individual students.

Recreational Activities and Residential Living

Since there is no Greek life at WWU, social life revolves around the many student clubs, organizations, and events on campus. The fun downtown and extraordinary range of outdoor recreation add multiple options for exploration in what is one of the most beautiful college campus locations anywhere.

The **Associated Students** organization is student-run and offers myriad services, facilities, and programs to foster a sense of belonging and encourage positive engagement, networking, and leadership opportunities. The **Ethnic Student Cente**r is one of those efforts and is home to student clubs focused on diverse identities, cultures, social change, and related activities.

There are eight multi-floor residential communities in the residential neighborhoods, some much newer than others, with various room layouts. Some residences have affinity group living/learning communities such as Pride Housing, Black Affinity, the Fairhaven Housing Cluster, and the Honors College. Each housing complex has its own dining commons plus there are cafes and markets and students can eat at any of these venues.

Indoor and outdoor recreation programs and facilities are substantial at WWU. Athletes, exercisers, and performers can get personal coaching through the **Center for Performance Excellence.** The **Student Rec Center** runs a full schedule of activities, including intramural and club sports, fitness, and exercise programs. The facility offers 3 basketball/volleyball courts, a 6 lane pool, cardio spaces, group fitness rooms, an indoor track, a climbing and bouldering wall, and a multi-activity court. The popular **Outdoor Center** offers a bike shop, gear rentals, excursions, challenge programs, and instructional clinics that offer certification programs in all wilderness and outdoor sport categories. The **Lakewood Boathouse** gives waterfront access for watersports. Varsity athletes compete in NCAA Div. II in the Great Northwest Conference.

Financial Aid

60% of WWU students receive some level of financial aid, including scholarships, grants, loans and student employment. 20.5% of students qualify for Pell grants. For out of state students, there are merit based awards such as the **Western Award for Excellence,** the **Western Achievement Award,** and a **Distinguished Scholars Award** and the University is a **WUE** participant.

Study Away

Global Learning faculty-led programs and Western Exchange, Internships, Independent Study, and a full range of study abroad organization programs are offered through the **Education Abroad** office. The **Global Ambassadors Club** encourages members to share their study away experiences.

Salish Sea Institute

The **Salish Sea** is a large and biologically rich inland sea that encompasses Puget Sound, the San Juan Islands, and the waters off of Vancouver, BC. The area spans from Olympia, Washington in the south to the Campbell River, British Columbia in the north, and west to Neah Bay. There are 419 islands in the Salish Sea, and the total population of the coastal communities is over 8 million.

Our PNW profiled colleges and universities in Seattle, Bellingham, Bothell, Tacoma, Lacey, and Olympia, WA, and Nanaimo, B.C. are all located on the Salish Sea coastline. Each institution has a stake in maximizing the health of this ecosystem and its related economies and communities.

These Pacific Northwest institutions, and many of their research centers, utilize the Salish Sea as a field laboratory for a wide range of courses, from those that address the politics of international boundaries to those studying urban wastewater systems engineering or the Salish Sea's endangered species.

WWU offers a unique minor in Salish Sea studies. The Salish Sea Institute convenes public conferences, produces reports to share scientific research and management strategies, and hosts a cohort of Research Fellows each year.

Western Washington University Basic Statistics

Undergraduate Enrollment	Freshman Class Enrollment	Institution Total Enrollment	Female/Male Student Ratio	Female/Male Faculty Ratio	Student/ Faculty Ratio
14,079	1,149	15,125	58/42	50/50	18/1
# of 1st Year Applications	**# of 1st Year Women Admitted**	**# of 1st Year Men Admitted**	**# of Transfer Students Admitted**	**Overall Yield**	**% of Out-of-State Students**
10,580	6,335	9,831	1,816	28%	29%
% Students Living in Campus After 1st Year	**% Fraternity/ Sorority Participation**	**% Students Receiving Need-based Aid**	**1st Year Students Retention Rate**	**% Classes Under 30**	**% Caucasian/ White Faculty**
27%	0	43%	80.4%	74%	83%
# Caucasian / White Students	**# Hispanic / Latinx Students**	**# Asian Students**	**# Black Students**	**# American Indian/ Alaskan, Hawaiian /Native Pacific Islander**	**# International Students**
9,519	1,505	900	260	79	140
In-State Tuition and Fees	**Room and Board Average**	**Out-of-State Tuition and Fees**	**Honors Program Cost**	**Honors Program Scholarship**	**Athletic Division**
$9,003	$13,080	$26,230	0	various	NCAADiv. II

Notes:

Fairbanks, Alaska

Yaquina Head Lighthouse, Newport, Oregon

SECTION THREE

Land Grant Universities

The term Land Grant refers to the funding mechanism of these distinctive public universities. **The Morrill Act**, establishing a land grant university in each state, was signed by President Abraham Lincoln in 1862. The Act provided each state with large sections of federal land, not only on which to build a specialized public university, but also to provide these institutions with a perpetual source of income from those lands.

The states receiving these land grants were obligated to establish at least one university dedicated to providing specific education and training in the agricultural and mechanical arts, along with other branches of learning as needed by their rapidly developing state economies.

Later legislation provided federal funding for research and experiment stations and outreach to all areas of each state through multiple Research and Extension service offices.

The 1862 legislation also required that the states provide access for Americans of all races and ethnicities at their land grant institutions. This led to some states establishing separate HBCUs *(Historically Black Colleges and Universities)* that mirrored their segregated public school systems, but all Pacific Northwest land grant universities were established as open access institutions.

There are 35 federally recognized tribal colleges and universities designated as land-grant institutions through the **Equity in Educational Land-Grant Status Act of 1994.** For reservation communities, these 1994 land-grant institutions help improve the lives and career opportunities of Native students and communities.

The 1994 institutions support research, education, and extension programs that enhance local agriculture and food production. The USDA 1994 Tribal Land-Grant Colleges and Universities Program ensures that these tribally controlled colleges and universities and the Native American communities served by these institutions equitably participate in the USDA workforce as employees and have access to USDA programs, services, and resources.

As you read the following six **Profiles** you will discover that today's land grant institutions continue to adhere to their fundamental mission of access, equity, and service. They emphasize critical research that serves and addresses problems of their state, nation, and the planet, concentrate on training the professional, scientific, and academic workforce of the future, and focus on experiential learning.

The land grant universities also staff the Research and Extension Centers throughout their states or territories and continue to

Skiing near Butte, Montana

provide critical education, training, and cutting edge research. They advance knowledge in support of regional and global agriculture, sustainable environments, human health and well-being, and safe communities.

Several of our PNW land grant universities manage newer federal grants for research, public education, and outreach, including **Sea Grants, Space Grants,** and **Sun Grants.**

These, like the original land grants, provide funding and resources to expand into critical research areas while encouraging partnerships with private industry, non-profit organizations, foundations, and local and state governments. These collaborations allow for research options, internships, and service experiences that greatly benefit students' career prospects.

The pace of innovation in the agriculture-related, health, and human sciences demands that knowledge rapidly reach people who depend on it for their livelihoods. The Cooperative Extension System, in collaboration with the **National Institute for Food and Agriculture (NIFA),** a critical partner of the USDA , is translating research into action: bringing cutting-edge discoveries from research laboratories to those who can put knowledge into practice.

Research and Extension Centers

All universities engage in research and teaching, but the nation's more than 100 land-grant colleges and universities have a third, critical mission — extension. The **Smith Lever Act of 1914** established a partnership between the U.S. Department of Agriculture (USDA) and the land grant universities entrusting these institutions with responsibility for applying research and providing education in response to the nation's critical agricultural, homemaker, and community needs.

That mission has evolved to meet changing needs, priorities, and environmental issues. Nonetheless, our land-grant colleges and universities remain the major resource for vital, practical, research-based information and guidance to agricultural producers, small business owners, consumers, families, and young people. Extension outreach includes related informational sites, publications, and sponsorship of 4-H and FFA Club activities for youth and is called the Cooperative Extension System.

The **Cooperative Extension System (CES)** is a nationwide, non-credit educational network that addresses public needs by providing non-formal higher education and learning activities to farmers, ranchers, communities, youth, and families in every state. CES maintains an extension office in or near most of the nation's approximately 3,000 counties.

County Extension agents help farmers grow crops, homeowners plan and maintain their gardens and homes, families provide safe and nutritional foods, and youth learn skills in self-sufficiency and leadership.

CES is more relevant than ever at this time of critical agricultural, food, and environmental challenges. It empowers farmers, ranchers, and communities of all sizes to meet the challenges of changing technology, food safety and nutrition issues, drought and wildland fires devastation, and the changing climate and weather patterns.

Above information was adapted from the NIFA website:
https://www.nifa.usda.gov/about-nifa/how-we-work/extension/cooperative-extension-history

University of Alaska Fairbanks

Fairbanks, Alaska /www.uaf.edu

UAF's unique Climate Scholars program is just one example of this far north University's innovative and interdisciplinary approach to curriculum and experiential learning for a diverse and adventurous student population.

Location

Fairbanks, with a population of about 32,000, is the second-largest city in the state. At 65 degrees north latitude, it is renowned for northern light displays, short winter days, and long sunrises and sunsets. Called the **Golden Heart of Alaska**, it is a base camp for expeditions to Denali National Park, a supply point for the North Slope oil fields, and the location of a large air force base. Tourism and mining are significant economic contributors.

Winter weather brings heavy snow and freezing temperatures, summers rarely see temperatures above the 70s, and humidity is comfortably low. Chena Hot Springs and snow sports offer popular winter activities, and the restaurant and pub scenes are active and varied. There is local bus transport, and Fairbanks International airport is served by Alaska Airlines.

Community

Student reviews compliment the friendliness and cultural diversity they find at UAF and report that the University listens to student concerns and welcomes their advocacy for changes.

A **Wilderness Welcome Orientation** is offered to new students, and the campus has traditional celebrations such as Starvation Gulch, which features bonfires to welcome students for the fall semester, and a Winter Carnival that involves the University and city with outdoor sports competitions and fun.

The **Festival of Native Arts**, a student-led tradition that brings together artists and performers, and the **Spring Fest** celebration, which features recreational, social and service oriented fun and games, are also community building events.

The **Honors College** and **Climate Scholars** students have access to intensive advising, flexible curricula, research opportunities, honors courses, and scholarships. These focus on creating opportunities for the student's community, supporting their personal goals, and enhancing career opportunities. The **Honors Makerspace** encourages collaborative problem solving and entrepreneurial projects.

Academics

UAF is the state's primary research university and home of two research stations, the Alaska Agricultural and Forestry Experiment Station focused on agriculture and forest sciences, and a Large Animal Research Station, which conducts long-term research on muskoxen, reindeer, and cattle. UAF classes are small, with 82% being under 20 students, and there are many opportunities for joining research teams. The UAF library is Alaska's largest, and holds one of the world's finest collections of Alaska and polar region materials.

The UAF campus has many impressive and innovatively designed buildings such as the **Engineering Learning and Innovation Facility**, a LEEDs Silver sustainable design facility. The innovative film and performing arts interdisciplinary program offers a unique focus on Alaska's current cultures, lifestyles, and environments. It utilizes the **Lee H Salisbury Theater**, a Lab Theater, the **KUAC Television** studio, the 1100 seat **Charles Davis Concert Hall**, and a Film Production Services program as professional learning workspaces.

The **Center of Arctic Security and Resilience** is one of the College of Business and Security Management program's major assets. CBSM's dual focus provides a unique perspective on potential careers, and its students have exceptional connections and multiple hands on experiences with the local business community, industries, and government entities.

Climate change is a focus of the **International Arctic Research Center** and the **Institute of Arctic Biology**.

The **Geophysical Institute** does research in seismology and volcanology and compliments the work of the Institute of Northern Engineering. UAF's Institute of Marine Sciences is a branch of the College of Fisheries and Ocean Sciences which operates the Sikuliaq, a 261 ft. ice resistant research ship.

Recreational Activities and Residential Living

Wood Center is the hub for student activities and home of the **Student Leadership and Involvement Office**, Student Activities, the Nanook Diversity and Action Center, and even a pub for older students, faculty, and staff. **Arctic Java** is a campus coffee shop and art gallery offering free shows and a stage for student and faculty presentations and art competitions.

Indoor UAF recreational activities are housed in the **Student Rec Center**, the Patty Ice Arena, and the Patty Center. The SRC has a multi-purpose gym area, weight room, indoor track, aerobics and dance floor, and cardio as well as a 2 story climbing wall and an indoor pool. Intramural leagues and competitions and other sports clubs are driven by student interest. The outdoor climbing wall becomes an ice climbing wall in winter, and there are miles of cross country trails for hiking, running, biking, and skiing. The **UAF Terrain Park** is open to skiers, snowboarders, and snow skaters of all levels. The **Outdoor Adventures** office organizes a full range of outings and trips and courses in ice climbing, sea kayaking and wilderness leadership, and more. UAF athletes compete in 5 men's sports, including ice hockey, skiing, and rifle, and 5 women's teams including skiing and swimming.

UAF offers a variety of housing options for students. There is a Gender Diversity Living/Learning community and a dorm with gender inclusive housing where students can live with a roommate of any gender, identity, or expression they choose, and there are gender specific floors. Older students have access to two-bedroom apartments, and there are family friendly accommodations as well. First year students in residence must purchase a meal plan. Recent student comments suggest the food has improved and selection is more varied than in prior years.

Financial Aid

UAF is a **WUE** participant. There are merit scholarships, including the **U-RISE Alaska** scholarships for students studying biomedical sciences, the **Nanook Brotherhood** scholarships for men of color, and a **Nanook Pledge** four year merit scholarship.

Study Away

UAF is a member of the **National Student Exchange**, through which students can apply for exchange at nearly 200 North American colleges and universities. Global Studies and language study majors and Honors students are encouraged to study abroad and can arrange credited study away. There is an intriguing theater course in Performance Studies with a study away project element that is faculty supervised.

Climate Scholars

The **Climate Scholars Program** in the UAF Honors College is the first of its kind in the nation.

It offers students the opportunity to work alongside some of the top climate scientists in the world in Alaska's unique ecosystems and most remote frontier locations. Theoretical knowledge is integrated with field-based learning and research while the students learn skills in Environmental Data Analysis, Visualization, and Effective Advocacy of climate change solutions.

Intensive field study expeditions take Climate Scholars to the Institute of Arctic Biology at Toolik Field Station just north of the Brooks Range, involve exploration of Permafrost Tunnels in Fox, Alaska, and engage them in research at Denali National Park, among other locations.

The program is a strongly interdisciplinary experience that connects the art, humanities, and sciences. It requires a semester long internship focused on climate change which can be science based or arts based.

Climate Scholars offers students the opportunity to study abroad through **The Climate Exchange,** which brings together a cohort of undergraduate students from around the world to engage in service learning and seminars on climate-themed issues.

University of Alaska Fairbanks Basic Statistics

Undergraduate Enrollment	Freshman Class Enrollment	Institution Total Enrollment	Female/Male Student Ratio	Female/Male Faculty Ratio	Student/ Faculty Ratio
5,892	538	6,879	61/39	33/67	7/1
# of 1st Year Applications	**# of 1st Year Women Admitted**	**# of 1st Year Men Admitted**	**# of Transfer Students Admitted**	**Overall Yield**	**% of Out-of-State Students**
1,402	48`	426	599	68%	18%
% Students Living in Campus After 1st Year	**% Fraternity/ Sorority Participation**	**% Students Receiving Need-based Aid**	**1st Year Students Retention Rate**	**% Classes Under 30**	**% Caucasian/ White Faculty**
19%	1%	48%	67.93%	94%	55%
# Caucasian / White Students	**# Hispanic / Latinx Students**	**# Asian Students**	**# Black Students**	**# American Indian/ Alaskan, Hawaiian /Native Pacific Islander**	**# International Students**
3,078	441	131	193	887	80
In-State Tuition and Fees	**Room and Board Average**	**Out-of-State Tuition and Fees**	**Honors Program Cost**	**Honors Program Scholarship**	**Athletic Division**
$9,882	$10,540	$10,787	0	various	multiple

Notes:

University of Idaho

Moscow, Idaho / www.uidaho.edu

This moderate-sized land grant university is noted for its wide range of research programs, leadership in cybersecurity, and the flexibility for students to plan an interdisciplinary curriculum that supports their chosen career paths.

Location

The thriving city of Moscow is located in northwest Idaho on the Washington-Idaho border at an elevation of 2579 ft. Moscow is only 10 miles east of Pullman, home of Washington State University. It serves as a commercial and agricultural hub for this eastern edge of the Palouse ecosystem, but U of I is the dominant employer.

Paradise Creek flows through the city, and there are seventeen parks and miles of trails, such as the **Bill Chapman Palouse Trail** that connects the two universities. The famous Palouse ecosystem has scenic rolling hills and a climate that supports the growing of crops like wheat, barley, beans, lentils, chickpeas, and canola in annual rotation.

This historic town offers abundant eateries and shopping options that cater to both the UI and WSU university populations; from fast food chains to those that serve locally sourced food and even a Bangladeshi restaurant. Breweries, wineries, pubs, taverns, and bars abound, many with live music. The Pullman-Moscow regional airport is served by Alaska/Horizon Airlines with regular flights to and from Seattle.

Community

In 2021 UI had 6372 full time undergrads and a well-balanced 49:51 male/female ratio. 32% of students are from out of state. Students comment on the friendliness and safety of the college town and the sense of care from the faculty and staff.

The **Women's Center** promotes and advocates for gender equity on campus and provides a welcoming place to gather, socialize, and develop educational and cultural enrichment events. Greek societies have a strong community presence at UI, with 20% of women and 24% of men participating, and leading much of the social life of the university.

Micron Foundation has given a large grant to U of I for the purpose of attracting a more diverse student community to its engineering programs by means of scholarships, mentors, and generous endowment of the **Micron Student Center.**

Academics

The majority of UI students are attracted to the traditional business, engineering, agriculture/natural resources, and conservation fields of study at land grant universities and to UI's wide range of social science programs. With a faculty student-faculty ratio of 16:1 about 56% of classes have 30 or fewer students.

UI is a national leader for **Cybersecurity Education** and is supported by government grants and industry partners. It is also home to several prominent research institutes, including the **Idaho Geological Survey,** the **Institute for Bioinformatics and Evolutionary Studies,** and the **University of Idaho Center for Secure and Dependable Systems.** These entities expand the range of undergraduate research, field work and internship opportunities for experiential education beyond the classroom and connect students with the institution's corporate and government research partners.

The University offers eight divisions, or colleges, that serve undergraduates and manages the **Sandpoint Organic Agriculture Center,** a Student Farm, a Dairy, Food Labs, and a Commodity Trading program. The **Integrated Research and Innovation Center** provides flexible space, labs, auditoriums, and state of the art equipment for interdisciplinary research by teams of faculty and students from all the UI colleges, including the **Martin School of International Studies**. A program in Organizational Sciences allows students the flexibility to select from different disciplines to meet management and administrative career goals. Movement Science is another interesting option that pulls from various courses such as dance, sports, exercise, and health and prevention in preparation for professional practice.

Recreational Activities and Residential Life

The **Office of Multicultural Affairs** connects with ethnic identity clubs, academic area-related organizations, and the Multicultural Greek Council. The **Student Recreation Center** has a one mile indoor track, multi-activity court, weight and circuit training areas, an enormous climbing center, two full sized gyms, saunas, wellness programs, and the outdoor program office. Intramural teams have a busy competitive schedule in which many games are between students representing their fraternities and sororities.

The **Outdoor Program** is extensive, with many trips, excursions, and outdoor recreation training options in everything from whitewater kayaking to fly fishing to Oregon coast surfing and backcountry skiing. The UI **Swim Center** serves the town and the university communities with two 25yd pools, an 8 lane pool, and a four lane shallow teaching pool. The facility also houses the Department of Movement Sciences, ROTC programs, and the women's swim and dive teams.

Sport Clubs are organized by students and enjoy intercollegiate competition in as many as eighteen sports, such as rodeo, water polo, climbing, baseball, lacrosse, and ice hockey, among others. Varsity athletes compete at NCAA Div.1 level.

First year students are required to live on campus. Choices include living/learning communities with academic themes, ones with various levels of support and guidance, gender inclusive and coed, and a variety of room layouts. These halls serve up to 1450 residential students. 1000 other students live in the thirty-four Greek chapter houses. Meal plans are required for first year students and for some other housing units. The main dining hall at U of I was recently transformed to provide a wider variety and more nutritious selections, and there are a number of smaller venues and a market.

Financial Aid

UI is a **WUE** participant, and even qualified students who are not from a WUE state are eligible for the **Invitation to Idaho Scholarship**. In-state students have access to merit based scholarships and state aid. Athletic scholarships are also offered.

Study Away

The **University Studies Abroad Consortium** offers opportunities for study away in many countries, including USAC Language and Culture Specialty programs. There are also shorter term faculty-led overseas programs regularly offered, and the International Studies degree actually requires an "abroad" experience.

Cyber Security Education

The federal Department of Homeland Security and National Security Agency have designated certain institutions as Centers of Academic Excellence for cybersecurity-related degrees. These centers, which include The University of Idaho, receive Scholarship for Service (SFS) National Science Foundation (NSF) Grants. These grants provide generous support for students who study in the fields of computer science and computer engineering.

SFS scholarship holders must agree to do an internship in a government agency during the summers between the academic years they are in the program. Then, upon graduation, they must work for a government agency for a time period equal to the amount of time the scholarship supported them.

To get an SFS scholarship the student must be a U.S. citizen, have advanced sophomore standing with the ability to graduate in two years, a 3.3 or better GPA, and strong recommendations. An upper division undergraduate SFS student receives a stipend of $25,000 a year and has all tuition and degree related fees covered, plus additional funds for books, health insurance, etc. and they are given dedicated collaborative office space. Each SFS student is assigned to a faculty-led research project on cyber security and cyber defense issues.

University of Idaho Basic Statistics

Undergraduate Enrollment	Freshman Class Enrollment	Institution Total Enrollment	Female/Male Student Ratio	Female/Male Faculty Ratio	Student/ Faculty Ratio
8,631	1,656	11,303	52/48	38/62	16/1
# of 1st Year Applications	**# of 1st Year Women Admitted**	**# of 1st Year Men Admitted**	**# of Transfer Students Admitted**	**Overall Yield**	**% of Out-of-State Students**
9,814	4,298	3,689	919	21%	28%
% Students Living in Campus After 1st Year	**% Fraternity/ Sorority Participation**	**% Students Receiving Need-based Aid**	**1st Year Students Retention Rate**	**% Classes Under 30**	**% Caucasian/ White Faculty**
39%	24%/20%	57%	74.57%	83%	85%
# Caucasian / White Students	**# Hispanic / Latinx Students**	**# Asian Students**	**# Black Students**	**# American Indian/ Alaskan, Hawaiian /Native Pacific Islander**	**# International Students**
6,498	961	174	91	91	255
In-State Tuition and Fees	**Room and Board Average**	**Out-of-State Tuition and Fees**	**Honors Program Cost**	**Honors Program Scholarship**	**Athletic Division**
$8,396	$9,898	$27,632	0	varies	NCAA Div I

Notes:

Montana State University

Bozeman, Montana / www.montana.edu

MSU gets applause from students for being a well-organized institution attuned to student needs and encouraging student engagement. The largest research university in the state, it is known for its interdisciplinary and hands-on approach to learning and a lively social scene.

Location

The city of Bozeman is thriving, not only because of the large university population but also because it has become home to dozens of tech companies. The area is famous for its surrounding mountains, proximity to Yellowstone National Park, ski areas such as Big Sky Resort, and other outdoor recreation.

The busy downtown provides many clubs, restaurants, entertainment venues, and fun community events. The city is located on a major highway and is served by Yellowstone International Airport. The city bus system is free.

Weather is very warm in summer and cold in winter. Bozeman has a wetter climate than the eastern portion of the state which results in lusher plant growth.

Community

Students report that they experience a strong sense of community and pride in the institution. Others mention that the university's various elements, from administration to sports, seem to connect, collaborate, and communicate in an organized way. They also note that the campus is attractive, easy to get around in, and has access to parks, trails and nearby wilderness areas.

The Greek community of eight fraternities and five sororities is rooted in years of tradition, and the members continue to impact the community service and social life of the campus. The student community does have a reputation for boisterous house parties.

The **Allen Yarnell Center for Student Success** at MSU fosters student engagement in the university community through a competitive points program that rewards students for their participation in events, activities, and programs, from tutoring sessions to sporting events.

Academics

MSU is the largest research university in Montana and is nationally recognized for its high level of undergraduate research. The College of Engineering's LEED Platinum building utilizes solar walls and a geothermal system for heating and cooling and transfers excess heat to nearby buildings forming an **Energy District** on the campus. 18% of students at MSU major in an engineering/computing field, but business, health professions, biology/life sciences, and family consumer science are also very popular majors.

MSU believes in a "learning by doing" model of education. The multidisciplinary **Undergraduate Scholars Program** offers research grant funding, travel grants, training, and support for students interested in getting started with research. MSU is a national leader in agricultural science research, and MSU's **Gianforte School of Computing** is a well-endowed program that provides high caliber learning experiences to students. MSU's student/faculty research teams foster many start-up enterprises.

Students can work with various MSU Institutes and Centers depending on their interests. The **Center for Mental Health Research and Recovery**, **Montana Institute on Ecosystems**, Montana's **NASA Space grant**, the **Spatial Sciences Center**, the **Museum of the Rockies**, and the **Center for Biofilm Engineering** are just a few options offered.

Honors College students take seminars capped at 16 students allowing for close interaction with faculty. They also have a choice of dedicated Honors housing. The College of Arts and Architecture offers an interesting BFA in Integrated Lens-based Photography and a major in Music Technology. Its School of Architecture students work on challenging community building and design projects for the **MSU Community Design Center**.

Recreational Activities and Residential Living

MSU fields over 25 student sponsored Club Sports, including Triathlon, women's and men's Rugby, Polo, and Taekwondo and others that participate in intercollegiate competitions. Intramural leagues make use of several recreation facilities including a large **Fitness Center**, gyms, and tennis facility. MSU Varsity Athletes compete in 7 men's and 8 women's sports, including rodeo, golf, and skiing at Div.1 in the NCAA.

The professionally staffed **Outdoor Recreation Program** uses the outdoors as a classroom focusing on developing leadership skills, building community, and fostering self-awareness. The program is expansive, offering trips, clinics, courses, a **School of Adventure Leadership** and 5 day backpacking Expeditions into wilderness areas especially geared to first year students. These offer some scholarship assistance. MSU presents an Annual Avalanche Workshop before each snow season.

The **Associated Students** organization serves as the voice of MSU students and manages many student activities such as **Catapalooza**, two days of music, food, and fun that welcome students to campus. The **Office of Student Engagement** manages funding and registration of the 283 student clubs and organizations active on the campus.

MSU residential services offer numerous **Living/ Learning Communities** in which 30-50 students with similar lifestyles and interests live together within areas of the residence halls. There are floors or wings of halls for Creative Arts, Business, Emerging Leaders, Engineering, and Honors students, coed and single sex halls and buildings. Mixed gender housing, in which students can share their suite with students of different gender identities, is available. **Hyalite Hall** houses up to 510 first year students in a brand new LEED Gold ultra-modern building.

Financial Aid

In addition to the **WUE** program, MSU offers renewable **Achievement Awards** of up to $10,000. **Blue and Gold Awards** are available to qualifying non-resident students. The prestigious **Presidential Scholarship** provides full tuition plus a stipend to outstanding students who demonstrate not only scholastic achievement, but also leadership and personal qualities. In-state students have several options for merit scholarships.

Study Away

MSU students can access 250+ study abroad programs, including Student Exchanges with MSU partner universities around the world. Engineers can gain International Certification with a study abroad program.

Computer Science

Over 50,000 students graduate with computer science degrees each year. The industry is highly competitive in terms of pay, and jobs in the field are growing faster than the national average. There is also a wide variety of positions for these graduates including in programming, software development, system administration, security applications, and more.

MSU's **Gianforte School of Computing** is gaining a new building to house not only the computing department but also related departments such as cybersecurity, optics and photonics, electrical and computer engineering, and creative industries. These programs focus on the interdisciplinary nature of computing to provide innovative educational and research opportunities and the new building's design will reflect this vision.

The Gianforte School offers both a bachelor of arts and a bachelor of science in computing and minors in both Computer Science and Data Science, and graduate degrees. A seamless BS/MS track allows ambitious students to get a Master's in C.S. within five years. The School has a strong record of obtaining grants for research and supporting entrepreneurial projects.

Montana State University Basic Statistics

Undergraduate Enrollment	Freshman Class Enrollment	Institution Total Enrollment	Female/Male Student Ratio	Female/Male Faculty Ratio	Student/ Faculty Ratio
14,668	3,868	16,841	48/52	54/46	18/1
# of 1st Year Applications	**# of 1st Year Women Admitted**	**# of 1st Year Men Admitted**	**# of Transfer Students Admitted**	**Overall Yield**	**% of Out-of-State Students**
11,421	10,509	8,972	1,258	15%	47.14%
% Students Living in Campus After 1st Year	**% Fraternity/ Sorority Participation**	**% Students Receiving Need-based Aid**	**1st Year Students Retention Rate**	**% Classes Under 30**	**% Caucasian/ White Faculty**
30.56%	5.34/4.49%%	37%	75.5%	69%	83%
# Caucasian / White Students	**# Hispanic / Latinx Students**	**# Asian Students**	**# Black Students**	**# American Indian/ Alaskan, Hawaiian /Native Pacific Islander**	**# International Students**
12,360	755	155	73	229	193
In-State Tuition and Fees	**Room and Board Average**	**Out-of-State Tuition and Fees**	**Honors Program Cost**	**Honors Program Scholarship**	**Athletic Division**
$7,726	$11,300	$29,604	0	varies	NCAA Div I

Notes:

Palouse region of Eastern Washington

The Palouse Ecosystem

It is no accident that both Idaho and Washington states chose to locate their land grant universities within the Palouse ecoregion. The serene and pastoral Palouse is a landscape unique in the world. It dominates the southeastern part of Washington State and some of northwestern Idaho.

Both of these land grant institutions have served the farmers, businesses, families, and communities of the Palouse region since being founded in the late 1890's. Research and scholarship at these neighboring institutions continue to focus on food, agriculture, and related science, engineering, health, and climate challenges that have global implications.

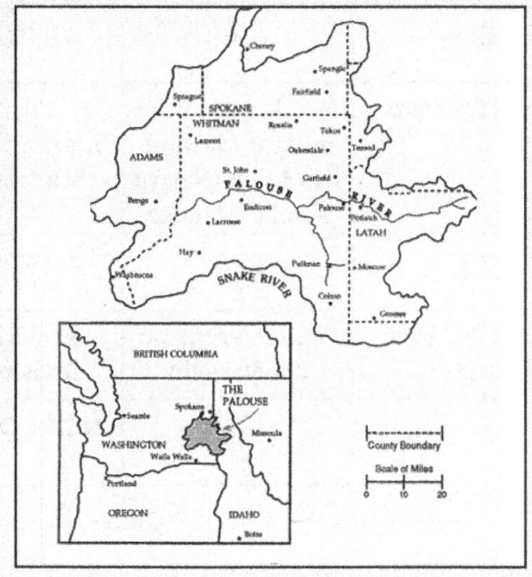

Richard D. Scheuerman, Palouse Country: A Land and Its People (1994)

Arboretum and Botanical Garden, Moscow, Idaho

Although these rolling hills look like dunes, they do not shift because they were formed tens of thousands of years ago during several ice ages. With extremely fertile soil, this is one of the most productive agricultural areas in the world. The fields, planted with wheat and legumes in alternating crop patterns, are breathtakingly beautiful in all seasons.

The same combination of climate, soil, and elevation that has made the Palouse one of the richest agricultural areas on the planet has also proven to be well suited for growing grapes. There are now two American Viticultural Areas designated within the Palouse, and these add to the thriving wine economy of the Pacific Northwest.

National Bison Range, Montana

Oregon State University

Corvallis, Oregon / www.oregonstate.edu

OSU offers a wide variety of activities and resources, diverse academic programs and research opportunities across many disciplines, and dedicated and enthusiastic faculty, on two thriving campuses.

Location

Corvallis is situated just off Interstate Highway 5 in the lovely Willamette Valley of central western Oregon, just 62 miles east of the Pacific Ocean and ninety miles south of Portland. A **Corvallis to the Sea** hiking/biking trail is a popular 2 day excursion and there is a regular bus route from Corvallis to Newport as well.

OSU is the major employer for the city. The climate is relatively mild, with snow being rare. Rain amounts are variable due to its proximity to the coast and the area enjoys around 200 sunny days annually.

Located on the Willamette River, Corvallis has 47 parks and natural areas, including one with a cross country course. The city of about 59,000 has plenty of bars, restaurants, beer pubs, the multipurpose Whiteside Theater, and the Darkside Cinema that all cater to the university population, as well as many community festivals, fairs, and a great farmers market.

Community

Although the main OSU campus is in Corvallis, a new, very innovative **OSU-Cascades** campus is growing in scenic Bend, Oregon. OSU has made progress in fulfilling its commitment to diversity and continues to move forward to provide not only equitable access, which is a shared goal of all land grant institutions but also inclusion and social justice priorities.

Student reviews are very positive about OSU and emphasize the welcoming staff, the supportive faculty, the very livable college-oriented town, and the University's multiple resources for student success.

OSU's **Cultural Resources Centers** contribute to an inclusive campus and shared sense of community. These are gathering halls and lawn spaces for students of various cultural heritages and identities to use for programs and social activities and foster a sense of home/community. OSU also builds community through programs such as the **Cultural Ambassador Conversant Program**. This introduces students from non-English speaking countries to a partner or partners to practice their English, learn more about U.S culture and social norms, and meet new friends.

Academics

There are eleven colleges within the university, including the College of Earth, Ocean, and Atmospheric Science, and OSU is nationally acclaimed for its research on climate change solutions. OSU is one of only three universities in the U.S. that have Land, Sea, Space, and Sun grants and the research projects supported by these grants provide many opportunities for undergraduate research.

Popular majors are in the fields of engineering, business, computer sciences, agriculture, and natural resources, biology and life sciences, family and consumer sciences, the social sciences, and parks and recreation. On the Corvallis campus 62% of classes have thirty or fewer students.

The new and much smaller Cascades campus offers one of only six Energy Systems Engineering programs in the U.S. This program combines engineering fundamentals with technical courses and business management. Also uncommon is an Outdoor Products interdisciplinary degree bolstered by the several outdoor product companies located in Bend. A close partnership with neighboring Central Oregon Community College provides financial benefits for students and direct transfer of credits.

On the Corvallis campus Biology students have a choice of eight majors, including Biological Data Science. Architectural Engineering, Ecological Engineering, and Bioengineering are among the fifteen programs offered in Engineering. OSU's nationally recognized Human Development Family Sciences program focuses on optimal child development, family trauma, age and disability challenges, and the fostering of community resilience and empowerment.

In the College of Business, there are management programs in Design and Innovation and in Supply Chain and Logistics. The College of Forestry, a world leader in outreach and research about the forest landscape, offers five programs on different aspects of this critical field, including a creative program in Renewable Materials.

The College of Public Health and Human Sciences focuses on diverse challenges for holistic health across the lifespan. OSU's **Hatfield Marine Science Center** offers student research opportunities and experiential instruction in Marine studies.

In all its programs, OSU is focused on experiential learning, research, community development, and collaborative service projects with local industry, businesses, government, and non-profits, and this pays off in internship options and future jobs for students.

Recreational Activities and Residential Living

The **Associated Students of OSU** serve as advocates for the student population. Students comment on the strong school spirit at OSU and the abundant opportunities to join clubs and organizations, attend a variety of events, and get support when you need it.

The Adventure Club at OSU is a student-led organization connected with the **Adventure Leadership Institute** and offers a wide array of outdoor programs, trips, and learning opportunities. Students can access the **Dixon Recreation Center** and the **McAlexander Fieldhouse** for recreational activities, fitness classes, intramural sports, and club sports. There are forty Club Sports, many of which compete with other colleges or at local and regional tournaments. Varsity athletes compete in NCAA Div. 1 /PAC-12.

OSU requires first year students to live on campus in one of sixteen residence halls that offer all the usual amenities. Single, double and suite style accommodations are available, an **International Living-Learning Center**, and a gender-inclusive community in which students can share with others of any gender identity. **Honors College** students have priority in one or more halls and **Innovation Nation** business students have their own living/learning communities as does the **Pride Community**.

Financial Aid

OSU is a **WUE** school. Pell eligible students can access the **Bridge to Success** program that covers the cost of basic tuition and fees and offers other support.

Study Abroad

OSU GO provides over 200 international opportunities for education, internships and research in more than 70 different countries around the world. Many faculty-led and course-related trips are offered to various countries.

Hatfield Marine Science Center

OSU's federal **Sea Grant** is one of thirty-four in the U.S. and supports oceanographic research and education. The HMSC is a costal campus for OSU and serves as a research base for six state and federal agencies. It is also a resource for K-12 educators and the public. The HMSC, located in the popular resort town of Newport, Oregon, provides OSU students with abundant research opportunities and housing.

A new building at the HMSC will have innovative classrooms and diverse labs, including an Innovation Lab for electro mechanical design and fabrication, a 250 seat auditorium, office space and meeting rooms for multiple collaborative and multi-disciplinary research projects and personnel.

OSU's **Department of Earth, Ocean, and Atmospheric Sciences** maintains a fleet of research vessels at the Ship Operations facility at the Center, and is designing the next generation of research vessels to advance coastal sciences with support of a $144 million grant from the National Science Foundation and other partners.

Oregon State University Basic Statistics

Undergraduate Enrollment	Freshman Class Enrollment	Institution Total Enrollment	Female/Male Student Ratio	Female/Male Faculty Ratio	Student/ Faculty Ratio
27,564	5,011	33,193	49/51	45/55	18/1
# of 1st Year Applications	**# of 1st Year Women Admitted**	**# of 1st Year Men Admitted**	**# of Transfer Students Admitted**	**Overall Yield**	**% of Out-of-State Students**
17,500	--	--	--	approx 25%	31%
% Students Living in Campus After 1st Year	**% Fraternity/ Sorority Participation**	**% Students Receiving Need-based Aid**	**1st Year Students Retention Rate**	**% Classes Under 20**	**% Caucasian/ White Faculty**
approx 17%	3,200	45%	86.8%	33%	83%
% Caucasian / White Students	**# Hispanic / Latinx Students**	**# Asian Students**	**# Black Students**	**# American Indian/ Alaskan, Hawaiian /Native Pacific Islander**	**# International Students**
72%	3,777	2,575	587	267	2,534
In-State Tuition and Fees	**Room and Board Average**	**Out-of-State Tuition and Fees**	**Honors Program Cost**	**Honors Program Scholarship**	**Athletic Division**
$13,191	$14,238	$34,983	$500 per term	varies	NCAA Div I PAC-10

Student enrollment at OSU-Cascades campus was 1247 with 252 students of color.

Notes:

Salish Kootenai College

Pablo, Montana, The Flathead Native American Indian Reservation / www.skc.edu

Students comment on the strong and kind support system and deep commitment to student success at this highly affordable college, which enrolls American Indian and Caucasian students from sixteen states and Canadian provinces, and fifty-three North American tribes.

Location

The **Flathead Indian Reservation**, located in scenic northwestern Montana on the Flathead River, is home to the Confederated Salish and Kootenai Tribes of the Flathead Nation. It comprises almost two thousand square miles of forest, mountains, and valleys supporting large populations of native wildlife.

The Nation includes most of the 30 mile long/16 mile wide **Flathead Lake** which is only 30 miles south of **Glacier National Park**. The reservation's population is under 30,000 and Native Americans are outnumbered 2:1 by other ethnicities. The Confederated Tribes own a hydroelectric dam that generates power for the entire region, several casinos and resorts, and electronics and defense technology firms with national and international clients.

Pablo is a college town with just over 50% Native American and 44% white population adjacent to the **Pablo National Wildlife Refuge** and a few miles south of the attractive lakeside resort community and trading center of Polson.

Although the winters are cold and summers are warm, the climate is moderated by the immense Flathead Lake. This region is a fertile farming area famous for its abundant cherry orchards. Glacier Park International Airport is 1.5 hrs. North, at Kalispell.

Community

The guiding mission of Salish Kootenai College is to empower students to improve their lives and communities through access to higher education and training, research, leadership, and service to their community. Students comment on the kind support system and deep commitment to student success at SKC.

As a Native American Tribal College, SKC aims to be a center of excellence for American Indian students, but enrollment is open and welcoming to all ethnicities and identities.

SKC's small, but internationally diverse college population represents sixteen US states and Canadian Provinces and 53 different North American Tribes. About 60% of students are either tribal members or tribal descendants and 70% are first generation college students.

Academics

Salish Kootenai offers 17 Bachelor's degree programs, 22 Associate Degrees, and six Certificate programs, and a Master of Science in Natural Resource Management and a Master of Education in Curriculum and Instruction. A BSN degree in nursing is associated with Providence St. Joseph Medical Center in Polson.

The College encourages culturally relevant instruction in all programs and works to both define and integrate cultural values into student and faculty/staff life. The college's 10:1 Student to Faculty ratio guarantees small classes and strong faculty support.

The Wildlife and Fisheries Department offers a research and technology-based interdisciplinary B.S. program in biology, ecology, management, and conservation of wildlife, fish and their habitats. Students in the program can specialize in an area of strong interest by choosing specific electives, fieldwork problems, and internships, and must develop and present a senior thesis.

The two-year Dental Assisting Technology program has students working in the onsite Dental Clinic within the second week of the program. It requires 300 hours of clinical externship with an emphasis on addressing the dental concerns of Native American communities, as well as their own communities. Education students have similar options for a Native Language Emphasis.

The BS in Hydrology requires Senior Research and Thesis Development and service projects, emphasizes placed-based issues and cultural perspectives, and design of scientific investigation that integrates climatologic, hydrologic, geomorphic, and ecological information and objectives.

The Life Science degree program emphasizes hands-on and place-based research experience with the program's two research labs: The **Environmental Health and Chemistry Lab** and the **Cellular and Molecular Biology Lab.**

Student projects are often funded through National Science Foundation, National Institute of Environmental Health Sciences, and other grants and are mentored by faculty. SKC addresses the critical need for expertise in forest fire issues by offering a Wildland Fire Emphasis program within the B.S. degree in Forestry.

Recreational Activities and Residential Living

The college community respects the **Student Senate** for its strong and well researched advocacy of student issues and concerns. The college's Student Activities Department works with the Student Senate to coordinate campus activities, and community wide events such as a Harvest Dinner, campus speakers, films, cultural activities, and talent shows and supports various student clubs and organizations. Students can join groups such as the **American Indian Science and Engineering Society, Spirit of Many Colors,** a gay-straight alliance, the **Forestry and Natural Resources Club**, and the **Student Nursing Organization**.

The Montana Campus Corps at SKS is affiliated with the statewide Montana Campus Compact that promotes volunteerism, public service, and service learning projects that have positive impacts for communities throughout western Montana.

The multiple-use **Joe McDonald Health and Fitness Center** has facilities for NCAA regulation basketball and volleyball and seating for 2500, an elevated running track, and demonstration kitchen. SKC offers men's and women's competitive Basketball and intramurals in basketball, softball, and volleyball.

The rugged western Montana environment offers a wide variety of outdoor recreation options, and camping, hiking, skiing, and rafting are popular group activities. **Flathead Lake State Park** at 2953 ft. elevation is 16 miles north of campus and has a long pebble beach for swimmers and opportunities for fishing, kayaking, canoeing, windsurfing, and board sailing. The **Wild Buffalo Rapids** of the **Flathead River** offer challenges for serious rafters and sea kayakers, and **Black Mountain Ski Area** is nearby.

On-campus housing is affordable but limited. There are also family apartments of different sizes available. Food service is limited to breakfast and lunch five days a week because on-campus residents have kitchens in their residences.

Financial Aid

Tuition and fees for out of state students are exceptionally affordable. Full time students who are enrolled tribal members and first generation are offered a tuition waiver for up to one year with potential for a 2nd yr. waiver if they meet a 3.0 GPA requirement at the end of the first year.

Students who are not enrolled tribal members, but who still qualify as being a Native American descendant, are offered lower tuition rates, as are Montana residents.

National Student Nurses' Association

NSNA is a fifty year old non-profit organization with 60,000 members. It is committed to building a thriving and diverse nursing workforce that provides leadership and quality education for improving the quality of life for all. Most state-approved college nursing programs have an on-campus chapter that provides mentorship and career information for students seeking licensure as registered nurses and offers access to resources. The NSNA Foundation offers undergraduate and graduate scholarships and School Grant Programs.

NSNA is active in national leadership and advocacy for the nursing profession. It supports life-long-learning, professional ethics and practices, and encourages a climate of caring among members. School chapter members have autonomy and independence to develop their own bylaws, policies, and procedures and are encouraged to take full advantage of their education, develop their professional leadership skills, attend the annual NSNA convention, and participate in its workshops

Salish Kootenai College Basic Statistics

Undergraduate Enrollment	Freshman Class Enrollment	Institution Total Enrollment	Female/Male Student Ratio	Female/Male Faculty Ratio	Student/ Faculty Ratio
690	160	716	67/33	62/38	10/1
# of 1st Year Applications	**# of 1st Year Women Admitted**	**# of 1st Year Men Admitted**	**# of Transfer Students Admitted**	**Overall Yield**	**% of Out-of-State Students**
--	--	--	--	--	--
% Students Living in Campus	**% Fraternity/ Sorority Participation**	**% Students Receiving Need-based Aid**	**1st Year Students Retention Rate**	**% Classes Under 20**	**% Caucasian/ White Faculty**
---	n/a	87%	65%	100%	--
%Caucasian / White Students	**# Hispanic / Latinx Students**	**# Asian Students**	**# Black Students**	**# American Indian/ Alaskan, Hawaiian /Native Pacific Islander**	**# International Students**
164	9	3	2	527	--
Tuition and Fees Montana non-Indian	**On Campus Housing (very limited)**	**Out-of-State Tuition and Fees**	**Honors Program Cost**	**Honors Program Grant**	**Athletic Division**
$5,076	$4,000	$11,583	n/a	n/a	n/a

Notes:

In Focus: Career and Technical Education

The Job Ready Option

Many high schools offer Career and Technical Education (CTE) courses, and these are popular electives for students, whether they are following a pathway to a four year college, have a strong interest in a CTE trade or profession, or are undecided about their post-secondary plans. At the post-secondary level, Career and Technical Education programs are referred to as the "job ready" option, offering documented skills training, on the job experience, and specialized knowledge and certifications that provide students with good employment prospects in the shortest time possible and at an affordable cost.

Technical training in electronics.

Public community colleges, technical institutes, and many universities offer such job-ready CTE programs in various professions and skilled trades. Options for affordable job training include State Apprenticeship Programs.

Here below are just a few samples of the many and varied CTE programs offered at our Pacific Northwest Colleges and Universities. Your local community college or higher education institution should be a resource for CTE post-secondary degrees in some fields. Since these home institutions will be most affordable, we urge you to explore your home options first. Nonetheless, we also hope that you will explore the specialized CTE programs, financial aid benefits, and tuition discounts offered by other institutions, both in state and out of state.

Highlands College of Montana Tech

Butte, Montana

Highlands is an example of a community college that benefits from being part of an outstanding four year public technical institution. Its most popular programs are in Civil Engineering Technology, Automotive Technology, and Metals Fabrication. As a WUE institution, it is highly affordable for out of state students and offers residential housing shared with the Institute's four year students. One of the housing units is called the **School of Minds Academic Intensive Community** and offers extended quiet hours, a computer lab, and dedicated study areas to enhance academic success. Highlands has career-ready and transfer pathways plus industry-specific partnerships that bolster its high job placement rate. In 2020 Highland's AS degree graduates scored a 96.97% job placement rate.

See the PROFILE of Montana Technical Institute in Section Two for more details on location and community life.

Renton Technical College

Renton, Washington
www. rtc.edu

Renton is a city of 100,000 in the southeast suburbs of Seattle on the shore of Lake Washington and is one of the most ethnically diverse cities in the U.S. RTC offers certificate programs and associate of applied science degrees in Advanced Manufacturing, Business Management, Culinary Arts, Health and Human Services, Information Technology, and Transportation Technology. The college's student population reflects the diverse community population of the city.

RTC's Medical Assistance and Medical Coding AAS degrees are highly ranked, and the college's completion rate of 63% and job placement rate of 85% mark it as one of the strongest institutions for vocational certificates in the U.S. RTC's **Construction Center of Excellence** serves as a model in developing partnerships among business, industry, and education to enhance economic and workforce development initiatives to meet current and future needs of the construction industry. 11 % of its students are enrolled in apprenticeship programs.

Renton also offers two very specialized programs. **Ford ASSET** is a joint effort of the Ford Motor Company, RTC, and a sponsoring Ford/Lincoln dealership. It is one of many RTC Associate of Applied Science degree programs that offer a **cooperative education component** *(a combination of classroom instruction and work experience)* and is the only Ford ASSET program in the State. RTC also provides one of only three AAS degrees in the entire nation in **Band Instrument Repair and Service**. Since both of these very specialized programs draw students from many other regions, RTC offers affordable housing to students who are enrolled in these programs. This is made available at nearby Bellevue College's brand new college dorm which offers suites and apartments and residential life amenities.

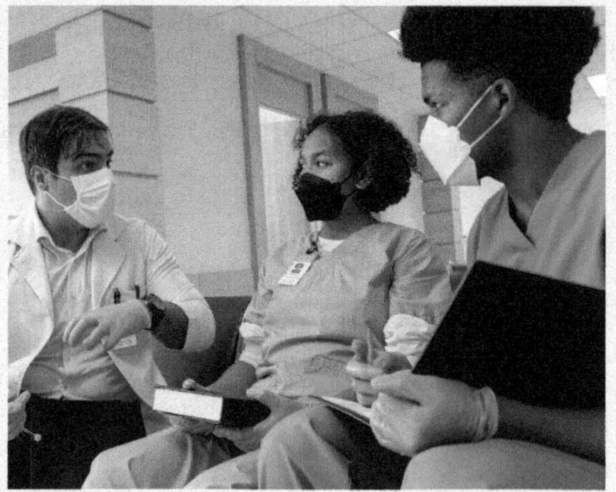
Nursing Students

Schweitzer Career and Technical Education Center at Lewis and Clark State College

Lewiston, Idaho

Home of seven Technical and Industrial Division programs, this new state of the art Schweitzer CTE Center serves LC State, Lewiston High School, and local industries. It is a community, state, university, and industry model of collaboration for addressing critical workforce training needs. The building has received Learning by Design magazine's 2022 Outstanding Project Award. The highly accessible LC State College offers Associate Degrees and Certifications in the Technical and Industrial, Business and Computer Science, and Business Technology and Service Divisions, Certifications in the Humanities Division, and four year degrees. *See LC State College's full PROFILE in Section Two for further information.*

Kenai Peninsula College

Soldotna and Homer, Alaska
www.kpc.alaska.edu

KPC is the fastest growing community college within the University of Alaska system. Its Kenai River Campus is located right on the edge of the 2 million acre **Kenai National Wildlife Refuge** and at the junction of two major highways. The Kachemak Bay campus is located 1.5 hrs. to the south, at Homer, Alaska, on the southern tip of the Kenai Peninsula. The community college's academic and training programs are designed to address both the abundance of natural resources and marine habitats in the area and the area's unique commercial, social, and environmental workforce needs.

KPC's programs of study include Alaska Native Studies, Anthropology, Fisheries Technology, and Marine Biology. It also offers training in Human Services, Liberal Arts, Medical Imaging, Paramedic, Firefighting, Instrumentation, Process Technology, and multiple Occupational Endorsement Certificates in fields such as Petroleum Technology and Conservation Ecology. KPC programs offer easy transfer to U Alaska's four year university programs.

Of special interest to students from other colleges is KPC's **Semester by the Bay** program. This program offers natural science students from around the country opportunity for intensive study and hands-on experience with cold-water marine habitats. The Fall Semester program focuses on marine mammal biology and issues of preservation and management. The Spring Semester program concentrates on conservation ecology and maximizes field-based experiences. Both programs can include internships with college credit and individual research connecting theory to practice. Students can rent apartments at the **Center for Alaskan Coastal Studies** or stay in other convenient lodging in Homer. *Check out it out at www.semesterbythebay.org.*

Portland Community College

Portland, Oregon / www.pcc.edu

PCC is typical of community colleges that serve a huge metropolitan area. Such areas offer myriad career opportunities but are also challenged by diverse economic and social needs. PCC is focused on workforce training to both meet these challenges and enhance employment options. It serves over 60,000 FT and PT students at four main campuses, ten centers, and offers forty-six different programs of study. These include Art and Communication, Business and Entrepreneurship, Construction and Manufacturing, Healthcare and Emergency, Public Service and Education, and Science and Engineering areas. The individual campuses host specific selections of these programs. Some of the most popular programs are limited in enrollment.

Such large city-based community colleges offer many facilities and activities similar to public and private four year institutions. PCC, for instance, has four art galleries, a 380 seat theater in its performing arts center, a creative writing program that produces five literary publications and a community magazine, recreation fields, a gym, and a competitive athletics program.

PCC is also an example of community colleges that offer **dual enrollment** with a nearby four year college or university. Dual enrollment allows students the option of taking some courses at PSU and others at PCC, or all courses at one or the other institution. There are **financial aid benefits** to these dual enrollment plans that can make the first two years of college very affordable, while still earning credits in university courses. *See the full Portland State University PROFILE in Section Two for more information.*

College of the Siskiyous

Weed, California

College of the Siskiyous is a community college that has made use of its location near the California/Oregon border to increase students' options and access. By attending COS, students who are residents of California can then transfer to either nearby Southern Oregon University or to the Oregon Institute of Technology and only pay Oregon in-state tuition. This reciprocity agreement is called **The Oregon Exchange**. It also allows Oregon residents to attend College of the Siskiyous at a discounted rate.

COS is also a member of the **Interstate Passport Network**. This program allows block transfer of course credits from lower division general education courses. The goal of the Interstate Passport is to eliminate unnecessary repetition of coursework achieved at a former college or university. Other PNW colleges and university members of the Interstate Passport Network include North Idaho College, Salish Kootenai College, U Alaska Fairbanks, Washington State University, and Western Oregon University.

COS offers AA degrees and Certifications in CTE fields such as Administration of Justice, Alcohol and Drug/Human Services, Nursing, EMT, Early Childhood Education, Business, Computer Science, Fire and Emergency Response Technology, and Welding. Its facilities include a 562 seat theater, gym, ample sports fields and training facilities, a science complex, and lodge-like student housing in a stunning mountain setting. *See the IN FOCUS on Community Colleges for further information on College of the Siskiyous.*

Vancouver Island University

Nanaimo, B.C.

As a regional university VIU is a less typical model of CTE higher ed institutions. VIU is a culturally responsive post-secondary institution committed to improving the educational opportunities of indigenous and marginalized students. It offers not only the full range of traditional four year, graduate, and post-degree programs common at such large public universities, but also a comprehensive **Trades and Applied Technology Division.**

The university's CTE focus is on career and professional development and valuable short term training that links students to employers and provides small classes with professional instructors. Nine of VIU's degree programs incorporate **Co-operative Education** that includes paid work experience for credit. New VIU students who are unsure of their career choice are enrolled in the university's EXPO program, where they can explore possibilities and interests with support from Education Advisors as they begin their academic coursework. *See the full VIU PROFILE in Section Two for further information.*

Washington State University

Pullman, Washington / www.wsu.edu

Although a large university, Washington State promotes a sense of belonging and strong school spirit while offering a wide range of academic specialties, research-based programs, and career pathways that encourage experiential learning.

Location

Pullman is a quintessential college town located in southeastern Washington on the south fork of the Palouse River at the Washington/Idaho state border. Like its close and slightly larger neighbor of Moscow, ID., Pullman's historical roots are in agriculture.

WSU and the international **Schweitzer Engineering Laboratories and Tech Center** are the major employers. WSU's student fees include a free pass on the town's good bus transit system, and Pullman is noted for its low crime rate. Pullman is built on four hills, with the downtown situated in the valley between them.

The climate is marked by warm, dry summers followed by cold and sometimes quite snowy winters. There are 21 parks and open spaces in the town and an eighteen-hole golf course, shopping, restaurants, and low-key nightlife. The **Regional Airport** has regular service to Seattle.

Community

WSU is a large university, but students consistently mention the sense of belonging to a tight-knit family, the helpfulness of staff, and the strong school spirit on campus. Greek life is prominent at WSU and members initiate many social and community service projects. A death by hazing at a WSU fraternity motivated passage of Washington State legislation prohibiting hazing and requiring state institutions to provide preventive education and oversight.

Student Centers promote understanding and appreciation of cultural and ethnic diversity, and a **Smart Start Program** supports first generation college students. A **Gender and Sexual Orientation Resources Center** serves the entire WSU system to advance equity and access, and is one of the sponsors of the UndocuQueer Conference to illuminate the commonality of undocumented immigrants and the LGBTQ+ community.

There are plenty of options for parties on the weekends, and varsity sports events draw enthusiastic crowds. Students from both U of I and WSU seem to enjoy the food options and entertainment amenities of both Pullman and Moscow, and there is an easy and friendly mixing of students from both campuses on evenings and weekends.

Academics

As a leading land grant research university, WSU offers research opportunities to ambitious undergrads and encourages experiential learning and internships in all fields of study. The most popular programs are in business, engineering, social sciences, communication/journalism, psychology, biological sciences, and the programs in agricultural and family and consumer studies. Within these broader fields WSU offers 95 different majors, almost as many minors and a hundred or more options for specializations with a major. 60% of classes have thirty or fewer students, while 5% have one hundred or more.

The Pullman campus also supports museums of anthropology, art, natural history, entomology, and two herbariums. The WSU Department of Agriculture receives significant funding for its research programs from the U.S. Department of Agriculture (USDA).

The **Murrow College of Communication** is noted for its research in media literacy and substance abuse prevention. WSU also staffs and manages NW Public Radio, NW Public Television, and the Murrow News Service, that give students access to professional training. WSU's **Pacific Northwest Center for Mestizo and Indigenous Research and Engagement** is the first in the Nation.

80% of **Honors College** students are engaged in research, and its curriculum offers small classes and an integrated and flexible curriculum. Major research facilities on campus include the **Geoanalytical Laboratory**, the **Laboratory for Atmospheric Research**, the **State of Washington Water Research Center**, and the **Nuclear Radiation Center**. WSU also has a **Phi Beta Kappa** chapter.

The University's **Center for Entrepreneurship** is a springboard for aspiring entrepreneurs with a focus on collaboration and hands-on skills and business planning. WSU's campus also has a Center for Behavioral Business Research and a School of Hospitality Business Management.

Recreational Activities and Residential Living

First Year Focus Living Communities are designed to bring faculty and students together in their resident halls, encourage group study of Core and 100 level courses, and discovery of all the options the campus offers for activities and services.

There are first year halls, a gender inclusive hall, coed, female only, male only halls, and several room and bathroom configurations. There are also special interests halls such as the Global Scholar's Hall, an Honors College Hall, and a Science, Engineering, and Math complex with its own fitness center, dining center, and café.

The WSU Cougars compete in NCAA Pac-12 athletics in eleven sports. Most students enjoy the university's huge intramural program, exercise at the **University Recreation Cente**r, or join a competitive student-run **Sport Club**.

WSU's **Palouse Ridge Golf Club** is considered one of the top two collegiate golf courses in the nation. The **Outdoor Recreation Center** offers innumerable options for trips, classes and clinics, and the 208 mile **Palouse Scenic Byway** offers many destinations for camping, biking, rafting, climbing and skiing, including at **Palouse Falls State Park**.

Financial Aid

WSU Cougar Commitment gives access to lower-income Montana students. WSU is a **WUE** participant (Cougar Awards program). There are also other scholarships based on GPA or demonstrated leadership.

Study Away

WSU offers exchange, faculty-led, and other global learning opportunities. Faculty-led programs in the past have included Social Entrepreneurship in Belize, Animal Systems in the World in Costa Rica, a Green Energy Study Tour in Denmark, a Designers View course in Paris and a Hearts in Motion Medical Mission in Guatemala.

Pacific Northwest Center for Mestizo and Indigenous Research and Engagement

The College of Education at WSU has founded a ground-breaking research, service, and engagement Center based on critical work that WSU's **Clearing House for Native Teaching and Learning** has been doing in the Washington public schools, including on reservations and in urban areas.

The Clearinghouse is focused on training public school pre-service and in-service teachers using the WA state Tribal Sovereignty Curriculum. The new PNW **Center for Mestizo and Indigenous Research and Engagement** is expanding this focus to include Latino/Mestizo populations, and developing innovative research, service, and community engagement programs.

The Center's mission is to address the needs of both Latina/o and Native populations and bring attention to the commonalities of the Mestizo and Indigenous experience, and the social, economic, and educational inequalities that challenge both populations.

The Center's research will be vital for the development of effective outreach and service programs targeting these diverse populations. It will also encourage collaboration and coordination of efforts among scholars, extension agents, staff, students, and community members and organizations. This work has national and global implications and will offer WSU students opportunities for significant research and service project engagement.

Washington State University Basic Statistics

Undergraduate Enrollment	Freshman Class Enrollment	Institution Total Enrollment	Female/Male Student Ratio	Female/Male Faculty Ratio	Student/ Faculty Ratio
21,272	3,872	28,843	54/46	--	16/1
# of 1st Year Applications	**# of 1st Year Women Admitted**	**# of 1st Year Men Admitted**	**# of Transfer Students Admitted**	**Overall Yield**	**% of Out-of-State Students**
--	2,154	1,718	--	--	--
% Students Living in Campus	**% Fraternity/ Sorority Participation**	**% Students Receiving Need-based Aid**	**1st Year Students Retention Rate**	**% Classes Under 20**	**% Caucasian/ White Faculty**
--	25%	--	81%	34%	--
# Caucasian / White Students	**# Hispanic / Latinx Students**	**# Asian Students**	**# Black Students**	**# American Indian/ Alaskan, Hawaiian /Native Pacific Islander**	**# International Students**
12,866	3,455	1,400	613	227	746
In-State Tuition and Fees	**Room and Board Average**	**Out-of-State Tuition and Fees**	**Honors Program Cost**	**Honors Program Scholarship**	**Athletic Division**
$12,416	$11,122	$27,7323	n/a	varies	NCAA Div I

Notes:

Further Resources

Recommended Reading

The College Conversation:
A Practical Companion for Parents to
Guide Their Children Along the Path to Higher Education
by Eric J. Furda and Jacques Steinberg | Sep 21, 2021

The College Conversation is a comprehensive resource for mapping the path through the college application process. It provides practical advice and reassurance to keep both anxious parents and confused children sane and grounded. Rather than adding to the existing canon of "How to Get In" college guides, or rankings, admissions experts Eric Furda and Jacques Steinberg provide a step-by-step approach to having the tough family conversations on this topic with less stress and more success.

College Essay Essentials:
A Step-by-Step Guide to Writing a Successful College Admissions Essay by Ethan Sawyer (July 1, 2016)

College Admission Essentials: A Step-by-Step Guide to Showing Colleges Who You Are and What Matters to You by Ethan Sawyer (July 21, 2020)

College Essay Guy maintains a vibrant on-line presence offering much free information and guidance. College Essay Guy is an excellent resource for practical, up to date, step-by-step guidance on writing college essays and putting together a college application. They offer both online courses and one-on-one services to help students navigate their college applications and pay for college. Best news is that they make their online workshops affordable for all and much information is offered for free, such as the Paying for College Guide.

Contact information: help@collegeessayguy.com, and
https://www.collegeessayguy.com/subscribe/paying-for-college
https://www.collegeessayguy.com/college-essay-resources

Pay Less for College:
The Must-Have Guide to Affording Your Degree, 2022 Edition, by Elizabeth Walter and Debra Thro (Author) (September 30, 2021)

This book offers detailed guidance on various processes and approaches to financial management of college costs. It offers an abundance of graphs and data to assist students, families, counselors, and mentors understand, strategize, and deal with the intricacies and frustrations of the financial aid process.

NOTE: The above books are available through your local Independent Bookstore or on Amazon Books.

The Edge Goldie Blumenstyk, senior writer at The Chronicle of Higher Education, covers innovation in and around higher ed in an informative and free weekly newsletter that brings attention to a range of issues such as first generation student priorities, how to put students on a path to success, and Pell Grant limitations.

Contact Information: https://www.chronicle.com/newsletter/the-edge

Inside Higher Ed This free service provides comprehensive, current, and reliable news and information and serves as a lively community forum for those who work in or care about higher education.

Contact Information: insidehighered.com

Links to Information Sites

Oregon ASPIRE

ASPIRE is the state of Oregon's mentoring program to help students access education and training beyond high school. The program matches trained, supportive, adult volunteer mentors with middle and high school students to help them develop a plan that meets their career and education goals.

https://oregonstudentaid.gov/aspire.aspx

https://youtu.be/cFdB7-TGeAc

Indigenous Scholars of Promise

This Bozeman MT. based college preparation program provides Native American or Latino High School Sophomores, Juniors, or Seniors with training, mentoring, and support services to help them prepare to apply to the schools of their choice.

https://www.hopamountain.org/indigenousscholarsofpromise

Advanced Opportunities

Advanced Opportunities is a program provided by the Idaho State Department of Education. The program provides funding for Idaho students to use for educational and career pathways.

https://www.sde.idaho.gov/student-engagement/advanced-ops/files/getting-started/program/2021-2022-Advanced-Opportunities-Booklet.pdf

Minds Matter Seattle

Minds Matter transforms the lives of accomplished high school students from low-income families by broadening their dreams and preparing them for college success.

seattle@mindsmatter.org

Northwest Education Access

Northwest Education Access provides comprehensive and individualized support to help low-income young people, ages 16-29, build their own path to higher education and beyond.

https://www.nweducationaccess.org/

The College Board

In addition to owning and managing tests like the PSAT, SAT, AP tests and the CSS Profile, the College Board provides resources, tools, and services to students, parents, colleges, and universities in college planning, recruitment, admissions, financial aid, and retention. Here are some links to these services.

https://www.collegeboard.org/

https://bigfuture.collegeboard.org/

https://bigfuture.collegeboard.org/pay-for-college/calculate-your-cost/net-price-calculator

CSS Profile: https:://cssprofile.collegeboard.org/getting started

U.S. Federal Government Higher Education and Training Financial Support

The U.S government provides grants and loans for post-secondary education and training based on family and student income and some special circumstances. Students may qualify for either grants that do not have to be paid back and/or loans that will accrue interest.

FAFSA

https://studentaid.gov/apply-for-aid/fafsa/filling-out

https://youtu.be/w9HWaQpuNSk

Federal Grants and Loans Program Links:

https://studentaid.gov/sites/default/files/federal-grant-programs.pdf

https://studentaid.gov/sites/default/files/federal-loan-programs.pdf

Special Circumstances Assistance

Fostered Youth:

https://www.acf.hhs.gov/cb/grant-funding/john-h-chafee-foster-care-independence-program

Independent Students:

https://studentaid.gov/apply-for-aid/fafsa/filling-out/dependency

Undocumented Students:

https://studentaid.gov/sites/default/files/financial-aid-and-undocumented-students.pdf

State and Regional Resources

State Higher Education Financial Aid and Awards Links

Alaska: https://acpe.alaska.gov/FINANCIAL-AID

California: https://www.csac.ca.gov/financial-aid-programs

Idaho: https://boardofed.idaho.gov/scholarships/

Montana: AwardMontana@montana.edu

Oregon: https://www.oregon.gov/highered/plan-pay-for-college/Pages/financial-aid.aspx

Washington: https://wsac.wa.gov/sfa-overview

Western University Exchange (WUE):

For basic information about WUE see In Focus segment on Tuition Discounts in Section One.

https://www.wiche.edu/tuition-savings/wue/

Student Support Services Sites

National Center for Students with Disabilities
www.nccedonline.org
www.nccsdclearinghouse.org

Mental Health
www.insidehighered,com/news/2021/09/20/colleges-expand-mental-health-services-students

Campus PRIDE
campusprideindex.org

Rise First

This online community site has multiple resources for first generation, low-income college students. Offers a Pre-college guide and links to scholarships for first gen and low income students in every state.

https://risefirst.org/

College Athletics Guides

NCAA Guide for the College Bound Student-Athlete

www.fs.ncaa.org/eligibility center/student resources/CBSA.pdf

NAIA Guide for the College-Bound Athlete

https://play.mynaia.org/media/1091/naia_guide_college_bound_student.pdf

529 PLANS

A 529 plan provides a tax-free way to save and invest for a child's education. When withdrawing the money from the 529 for qualified educational expenses any gains that may have accrued in the 529 investment fund are not taxed.

College Savings Investment Plans (529)
www.investor.gov/introduction-investing/general-resources/news-alerts/alerts-bulletins/investor-bulletins-10

SAT PREP

The nonprofit KHAN Academy offers free practice exercises, instructional videos, and a personalized learning dashboard that empowers students to study and practice at their own pace.

www.khanacademy.org/test-prep.

Other free SAT Prep Resources are listed on the ENACT Your Future, Inc. website.

https://www.enactyourfuture.com/free-sat-resources.html

Gap Year and Study Abroad Program Sites

IE3 Global-Oregon State University
https://ie3global.org/contact/

Verto Education Gap Year
https://vertoeducation.org/

National Student Exchange
https://www.nse.org/

GEO- Global Education Abroad
https://geo.uoregon.edu/

International Student Exchange Gap Year Abroad
https://iseusa.org/travel-study-abroad/gap-year-program/

American Institute for Foreign Study (AIFS)
www. aifs.com

Highlight Topics Index

Index to Colleges and Universities

Acknowledgements

THIS REGIONAL GUIDEBOOK evolved to fill a gap in the national coverage of higher education opportunities in the Pacific Northwest. We deeply appreciate the assistance of the many Institutional Research and Admissions Staff who willingly provided statistical information for their institution's profile in time to meet our deadline. Their enthusiasm for the project helped sustain our energy.

Our friends and colleagues in the Ashland High School ASPIRE mentor group supported and encouraged this project from the beginning. We especially thank Richard Krieger, a deeply committed Oregon ASPIRE mentor and educator, for his donation of the evocative cover photo, Adrienne Simmons, for her ability to recognize potential in our most vulnerable students, and Jen Marsden for sharing her knowledge and skills as a gifted college and career counselor and Oregon ASPIRE program director. Their determination to identify and locate the resources each individual student needs to access and thrive in post-secondary education has been an inspiration for this book and its themes of inclusion, innovation, and equitable access.

We greatly appreciate gifted cartoonist Dave Coverly's generosity in donating use of his classic "raised by wolves" cartoon about college essays. Thank you also to Adrian Sanchez Gonzalez, Staff Photographer, and Dr. Christa Merzdorf, Associate Professor of Cell Biology and Neuroscience, Department of Microbiology and Cell Biology at Montana State University, for permission to use their photo from a summer hands-on research program for Montana tribal college students. We are also grateful to Palouse Heritage for permission to use the Palouse Region map illustration.

The multi-faceted talent of local book designer Chris Mole' has been essential to the success of this project. We are fortunate to have her as a professional partner. She quickly grasped the purpose and potential of the guidebook and not only applied her skills to enhance it, but dealt with corrections and changes with grace and patience.

Kudos to all the college and university staff and consultants who compiled, wrote, and designed the institutional websites from which we have gleaned not only factual information, but also a sense of each institution's unique community and mission. We hope our student readers accept the invitation to delve deeply into the websites of the colleges and universities mentioned in this regional guide and get into contact with those that seem to be a good fit for their social, academic, and career interests.

We have great admiration for the caring high school college and career counseling staff and other youth mentors who devote energy and expertise to help aspiring students gain access to postsecondary education and training. We designed this guided exploration of PNW colleges and universities to be a beneficial new resource for you and look forward to your feedback.

Navigations2College is deeply grateful for the generous financial support of this guidebook project provided through the Walter D. Collins estate.

About Navigations2College

NAVIGATIONS2COLLEGE IS A SMALL NON-PROFIT ORGANIZATION headquartered in Ashland, Oregon. We support and engage in local efforts to provide equitable and inclusive access to higher education and training for high school students through affordable college and career services and information. The Pacific Northwest Colleges and Universities guidebook is our initial publication.

Sarah D. Silver, M.A.

Sarah Silver is the founder of Navigations2College and currently serves as its Executive Director. She has had an extensive career in college and career counseling and in rural community education and program development. Sarah has served as an instructor in education for Colorado Northwestern Community College and Prescott College, and is a published author.

Board of Directors

President: Ana C. Patel, B.S. Lewis and Clark College, MIA Columbia University.

Vice-President: Bowman Cutter, B.S Macalester College, PhD. University of California Los Angeles.

Secretary: Gallo Crane Patel, University of Chicago, Class of 2025.

Treasurer: Dean L. Silver, B.S. Massachusetts Institute of Technology.

Executive Director: Sarah D. Silver, B.A. George Washington University, M.A. Prescott College.

Equitable and Inclusive Access to Higher Education and Training is a Matter of Social and Economic Justice

Made in the USA
Columbia, SC
20 October 2022